The
Freedom
Element

Living with

H y d r o g e n

Dr. Addison Bain

The Freedom Element

Living with

H y d r o g e n

BLUE NOTE BOOKS
F L O R I D A

Blue Note Publications, Inc.
Cocoa Beach, Florida
www.bluenotebooks.com
1-800-624-0401

ISBN 1-878398-97-0

Library of Congress Control Number: 2004111108

First Edition

Cover Design by Carmen Abreu
Cover photograph of hydrogen powered car courtesy of BMW

Printed in the United States of America ⸺

To the younger generation around the world in hopes that many are inspired by science, math and engineering and apply their knowledge to enhance our quality of life on this planet.

* * *

The greatest challenge in implementing the hydrogen economy is not so much a technical and cost issue as it will be the proper and adequate education of the general public; those not yet a member of the hydrogen family.

CONTENTS

Acknowledgments

I wish to recognize the effort on the part of Laura Marie (Leonard) Lecire for her publishing knowledge and editing skills. As a writer herself, Laura Marie was able to provide the necessary spark in the dialogue bringing many people to life in the book. Her enthusiasm and attention to detail make the story about the author enjoyable reading.

I am indebted to publisher, Paul Maluccio, for his keen ability to keep the storyline in focus and on track.

Sharon, my loving and understanding wife, with her many ideas and suggestions along the way, provided me the inspiration to make the book project worthwhile.

A POEM BY MOM

Our First Born

Away back in 1935 the good Lord sent us a son,

A cute chubby five pounds with big blue eyes and a blonde curl,

little did we realize his future as we named him Addison.

He was an excellent student especially science and math were fun,

Inquisitive mind, had to learn what made everything run.

Always building model rockets, and a space station so real,

Made us wonder if his design they did copy and steal.

His room upstairs looked like a rainbow with model paint,

Probably here and there are still dabs, some very faint.

We had fun fishing, camping, picnicking, Dad's favorite pastime,

then it was off to college and into the service that fall,

Which was great and helped him into his desire for rockets,

space and all.

He didn't let marriage or family stand in his way,

On up the ladder, positions and degrees he did stay.

He made hydrogen and Hindenburg world known to respect,

The name Dr. Addison Bain well known on the Internet.

Look at him at the top, all retired now,

Writing this book sharing his years of world research and how.

Dorothy Riebe Bain

Introduction

Life springs from hydrogen, and as fate has dictated, the subject of hydrogen has permeated my life. For a long time, family and friends encouraged me to write a book.

My challenge was to take on a topic that could generally be considered a dull one, and make it interesting. As I reflected on my adventures and misadventures with hydrogen, I realized that it has been intertwined in so many aspects of my life. Therefore some parts of the book may appear like a memoir even though that is not the focus or reason for writing this book. Never the less I do include a few stories about myself so the reader doesn't think I had a life just with hydrogen! It is important, however, to provide the reader an understanding of my background and the evolution of my relationship with the fundamental element, hydrogen. Some relevant facts and events have been included, as I have found that they are not well known.

My overall goal is to dispel many common misconceptions about hydrogen, convey how important it is to everyone and make the story interesting and informative for the general public. *The Freedom Element, Living With Hydrogen,* includes a brief story about my life growing up in Northwest Montana where I developed a keen interest in science. I moved on to serve in the US Army working with rockets, and then the adventures of a long and successful career with NASA. Along the way, my experiences in working with various machines prepared me for developing hydrogen machines later on. Many people inspired me. I am especially honored to have worked with Dr. Wernher von Braun's rocket team.

This book will also tell you of my one-man crusade to exonerate hydrogen from the *Hindenburg* disaster. Most people think that hydrogen is what initiated the fire. I'll give you an explanation of the infamous disaster based on modern forensic techniques and evidence never released to the public. The book goes into considerable detail, but it is my opportunity to finally publish my work on the full story and reveal the "smoking gun." I have chosen to publish my research in a public forum rather than a scientific forum.

At the heart of the book is the importance of hydrogen to our daily lives, its partial solution to the world's energy crisis, and how it can someday release the world from the shackles of the petroleum czars—thus the title, *The Freedom Element*.

Chapter 1

The Early Years

According to popular theory within about three and a half minutes after the beginning of the "era of quantum gravity" (shortly, very shortly after God said, "Let There Be Light"), roughly 13.7 billion years ago, protons, electrons and other subatomic particles—the basic ingredients to eventually form hydrogen and other simple atoms—were born. Approximately 380,000 years later, the Creator's hand began to mold hydrogen, the element that went on to make up most of the universe as we know it today.

Along about the fall of the year of our Lord 1935, another miracle took place. It seems the Creator had set aside a small handful of hydrogen, just the right amount to flow into a mix in Kalispell, Montana. Out of the blend came a bouncing baby boy, namely me.

"Thanks God!"

In the mid 1930's, Kalispell was a small town of about 8,000 people. Small to the rest of America, it was a large town for Montana. Lumber, ranching and some limited silver mining were the major industries. With a backdrop of the snow-capped mountains of the Continental Divide, and the panorama of the Flathead valley, Kalispell, together with its neighboring towns, felt like a vast farm. It was friendly and a good place to grow up.

Dad was a short fellow, stocky and very muscular. He didn't attend high school but worked in an auto radiator shop to support his mom and five siblings. He was born near Kalispell and his first job was that of a lightweight boxer. After that, he became what was known as a "powder monkey" —someone who worked with dynamite on road construction projects. He also went on to become a heavy equipment operator, building roads for the US Forest Service. But, for most of his life, he worked in auto mechanics.

Dad read incessantly about medicine, science and technology. His dream was to be a medical doctor, but the struggle of supporting many family members never allowed that to happen. Many dreams were laid to rest during the Depression years.

Mom was tall and slender and pretty. She grew up in a homestead environment about 30 miles from Kalispell. She was raised in a log house—the logs had been hewn with nothing more than a broad axe. When she was growing up, they had no phones, no transportation and no stores. Her environment was nothing but the land and determination. Despite this humble beginning, she went on to be a schoolteacher. She taught kids in a one-room schoolhouse.

Mom had a natural artistic talent and a few years later she took up monogramming to help supplement Dad's earnings. She was very good at it and developed her own little business. That, combined with Dad's hard work, allowed me to go to school and enjoy a few little extras.

As a young boy, I was extremely shy, especially around girls. They often followed me home or pulled pranks on me at school. My main interest, however, was not them; it was science. I think I was in the fourth grade when I got my first chemistry set. After that, I spent hours in the basement. At first, I followed the instruction manual to gain an understanding of how different chemicals interacted, and then I began developing my own fuels for the model rockets I built.

In those days, I was pleased that my folks were able to do what they did. They had a variety of talents and passed along their enthusiasm for their interests to me. I learned from their example and followed suit, helping out when I could. For example, I raised a victory garden and sold seeds and greeting cards to raise some money to buy materials to make model airplanes and rockets. During the war years, our family saved string, paper, and especially tin foil. Periodically, someone would come by the house and collect these items for the war effort.

I was in the third grade when Dad gave me my first model airplane kit. It was a replica of the B-17 Flying Fortress. It was quite a challenge to construct. I had to use a razor blade to cut out the hardwood pieces. Later models came out using the softer balsa wood. By then, Dad found an X-acto set for me. It had nice sharp tools designed especially for model builders. As time passed, I became more interested in model airplanes. I could not afford the kits, so I usually built the planes from scratch, guided by photographs of airplanes that I clipped from magazines.

I had seen numerous photos of the German V-2 rocket and the idea of building a replica from scratch took hold. Instead of handing over everything to the war effort, I kept back and squirreled away some tin foil. From small strips of pinewood, I constructed a two-foot airframe model of the V-2 and covered it with the foil. With the finishing touches complete, I stepped back to admire my handiwork. I think it was at that moment that I became obsessed with getting it off the ground.

I read that the V-2 took alcohol and liquid oxygen for propellants. I could probably have come up with the alcohol, but I realized how ridiculous it would be to make the engine let alone worry about the oxygen. Maybe some stuff from my chemistry set would make a good propellant. I don't know why at the time I thought my ignition system should be 120-volt household electricity. But a good shock and a large puff of smoke was the end of that experiment!

My next rockets were a little better, but Mom grounded me for putting burn holes in the folks' lawn. Dad really loved to have the best looking yard in the neighborhood. I was smart enough to move my rocket operations to a vacant lot.

Around the age of ten, my friend Burt and I used to go to the Orpheum Theater about once a month. Each time, Mom gave me ten cents, nine for the movie and a penny for the candy or gum. On one occasion, we saw a fantasy film about outer space where some of the characters used ray guns

Model rocket launch

to do battle with their enemies. Well, that was it! We had to have one, too; so soon as we got home, we got to work. From materials that Dad had acquired from the lab at the refinery where he worked at the time, we built our ray gun. We planned to scare the neighborhood girls with it. It was a wild-looking contraption with glass test tubes and spiral cross-flow glass tubing. The hard rubber barrel was two inches in diameter and three feet long. It was mounted on an old surveyors instrument tripod. We filled the steel breech with powder extracted from a box of firecrackers. When lit, it would burst out with a startling bang and an impressive flame. My first chemical engineering project!

Another movie that came to the theater, *Destination Moon*, also left its mark on me. After I saw it, I proceeded to build a four-foot tall rocket model out of hundreds of pieces of balsa wood — a material new to me. It had two small quartz windows where you could look inside to see the control room that was illuminated by several 1.5-volt lights. That rocket wasn't destined for flight. It was for show and tell only. I used it at school as a prop for my speeches on space travel. It was displayed in the window of downtown Kalispell's one and only department store for quite some time. This continued to inspire me to maintain an interest in rockets. Today it sits on a lunar landscape in my office, complete with model astronauts and a lunar rover.

When junior high school began, I started to spend more time hanging around buddies Ed and Sid. We were like three musketeers. Ed had the money. His folks discovered oil in the eastern Montana town of Cutbank before they moved to Kalispell. Sid always had a good job and was fond of model airplane engines. While he worked at the local model shop we got a lot of "good deals" on stuff we needed for our airplanes. Ed was the flier. We used Sid's engines and my airplanes, and Ed would crash them. It wasn't deliberate. It was just that my designs were a bit weird. I acquired two pulse jet engines from Sid and a rare titanium/aluminum fuselage. The jet engine was rated at one horsepower, put out four pounds of thrust, and ran on white gas (gasoline in the days before leaded gas). I spent considerable time shaping the special fuselage to make it aerodynamic. I also formed it to fit the arc of a 75-foot radius circle, which was the length of the control wires. We achieved 150 miles per hour to the surprise of other modelers. They were designing theirs with swept back wings and razor-edge-leading surfaces analogous to the air force jets. I used an airfoil design from the WW1 type prop planes. I told the guys they flew planes at 150 miles per hour in those days, not the 500 mph they were designing to. That was my favorite model airplane, and I never gave it away like I did the other models.

Around that same time, I built a mahogany boat about four feet in length and used the other pulsejet as the engine. I worked on the model boat for about a year, cutting and putting together the narrow strips of mahogany. I installed an asbestos cover under the engine and designed airflow channels to permit cooling airflow across the engine while the boat was operating. The key to using the jet engine was to make sure the boat did not run "on the ground" more than a few seconds. If it did, the combustion chamber would heat up to one thousand degrees and incinerate the model. Designed into it was a stainless steel assembly whereby a fly wire could be attached to control the boat.

* * *

I really enjoyed high school classes, especially math, science and biology. I had a hard time with speech for I was horrified to get up and give a talk. Mom told me to pick an interesting subject above the norm and present it like you know what you are talking about. So, I built a model space satellite and prepared a poster showing how a rocket takes it into space and orbits the earth. Thanks to Willy Ley's early book that dealt with rockets, missiles, and space travel that I found in the Kalispell library; I was able to put together my speech on space travel. The class loved it. The teacher pooh-poohed the possibility of flying into space, but she gave me a good grade nevertheless.

I think the Ley and von Braun writings had the most inspirational impact on my early school days. They underscored my desire to take all the math and science the schools could dish out. Mom and Dad encouraged it since I brought home good grades in those areas. Dad became interested in reading about space and the cosmos, too.

Mom still talks to people about the space station I built and hung from my bedroom ceiling. She thinks I designed it from scratch, and NASA later copied it. Actually, the space artist Chesley Bonestell influenced me quite a bit.

* * *

In high school, I bought a 1936 Ford from Sid. Dad assisted me in working on it as well as teaching me auto mechanics. Sid got a Vincent Black Shadow motorcycle capable of 140 mph, and we all read a lot about souping up machines. We tore down the '36 Ford and "improved" the engine. Sid let me take the Vincent out but 122 mph was fast enough for me; especially since Sid was behind me, trying to catch up with Dad's '49 Packard. Those were the days of me learning a lot about machines.

On a particular quiet Sunday morning, Sid made arrangements to pick up a few gallons of high-octane aircraft fuel and some nitro methane from his stock of model airplane fuel. We took the '36 Ford to the top of Sundown Hill on US Hwy 93. Sid raised one side of the hood and tinkered with the carburetor. I drove. Ed sat next to me and handled the floor shift. Sid sat in the backseat to observe the speedometer over my right shoulder. I had practiced "snapping the clutch," while Ed shifted. We practiced on our local dirt track to get experienced with the procedure. I snapped the clutch to keep from losing too much engine rpm in shifting the transmission. Ed had to almost read my mind as he shifted to keep from leaving transmission parts all over the road.

We started the run.

Sid called out, "Thirty-nine, forty, forty-one mach point –shift," Ed slammed it into second. "Seventy-one, seventy-two, seventy-three mach point–shift," Sid yelled.

At a speed of 101, our goal, Sid screamed, "shut her down." I hit the brake pedal and Ed pulled on the emergency brake lever. The next few seconds seemed like an eternity. There was US Hwy 93, curving to the right, and the church was dead ahead. Oh no! We don't need Ford parts in the front pew! I managed to "drift" the '36 to the right as we had practiced on the dirt track. We avoided disaster. The brake (control) system was not the modern auto hydraulics of today but a system of wires, levers, pulleys and cams just like that used on the '36 Airship *Hindenburg* control systems. Amazing! We let the engine cool down as the radiator was belching steam (must have been the "hot" fuel mix of high octane gas with model airplane fuel we used).

* * *

There were so many teachers who gave me direction during high school. Mr. Nelson was my high school chemistry and physics teacher and I will never forget how closely he worked with his students. He was perhaps one of the most influential persons in my life in regards to learning science. We nicknamed him "Newt" after famed physicist Sir Isaac Newton. He made it fun doing experiments in the chemistry and physics labs. I must say, I think I got all I could out of high school. Mr. Wilson ran the auto mechanics and electrical shops and Mr. Custer ran the wood working shop. They inspired me, too. Custer was a short stocky man who never smiled. He was very strict about teaching safety in the shop. When you were through with the lathe, planer, table saw and other power tools, you made sure they were cleaned up after each use. Woodworking became one of my favorite hobbies.

After high school graduation the summer of '53 was on me and I needed a good job to continue saving for college. The previous summer, I had worked in the county court recording office drawing up land plats, using what I had learned from my high school classes in drafting. Later I worked for a land surveyor learning the basics of that trade, but they didn't pay well.

Dad got me on at Schomers Motors where he was shop manager. I started out doing oil changes and lube jobs. One of Dad's mechanics took me under his wing and let me work with him on engine overhauls and brake repairs. This did not fare too well with Dad. As Mom later told me, he was afraid I might like it too much and want to make a career out of auto mechanics. So, a friend of Dad's got me on the construction crew of a new aluminum processing plant being built in Columbia Falls about twenty minutes from Kalispell. I started at a buck and a quarter an hour, with double time on Saturday. Boy! I hit pay dirt.

Dad would take me fly-fishing to a place called the Twins. Twin Creeks were located in a wilderness area called Spotted Bear. It was about 65 miles from the nearest town. The road wound through deer, elk, moose and grizzly bear country.

Dad liked to read about astronomy. At night we would lay in our sleeping bags on the ground next to the bubbling sound of the Upper Twin and look up into the night sky. At that latitude and elevation and away from the lights of civilization, it is a sight not many people ever witness. You would swear you could reach up and grab a star or one of the planets. The Northern Lights would shimmer in red, green and yellow colors.

Dad would say, "Aurora borealis."

I said, "A roar of what?"

He explained how thin our atmosphere is, that during the day there is this false sense of security we have with the scattering of clouds, the blue sky and sunlight.

"We are traveling at a very high rate of speed through space," he continued.

Just then a meteor streaked across the sky and ended with a big burst of colored light.

I said, " I see what you mean."

Dad went on to talk about what he was reading concerning the heavens.

"You know you are looking at a lot of hydrogen."

"And?" I queried.

"Yeah, that's the stuff that makes stars work," he replied.

I told him of making it in the lab when I was in high school, using a battery and electrode set up and splitting the water. I explained how Newt showed me how careful I needed to be when I put a lighted match near the bottom of the inverted test tube—the one with hydrogen in it. You could not see it but it made a loud puff.

Dad fortified me with books on the cosmos to take to college for "casual" reading. That influence still exists today as I enjoy reading about cosmology.

* * *

Next it was college. Ed, Sid and I checked into the "low income" dormitory called the Hudson House in Bozeman, Montana. The rich guys had their fraternities and some lived in local apartments, but the dormitory "barn" was cheap. It was, in fact, a converted sheep barn! The Dorm was fun. School was the typical grueling day-to-day sessions of chemistry, physics, language, and so forth. For some reason, I enrolled in the nuclear physics program. Ed took up mechanical engineering and Sid decided on medicine. Ed was good at mechanical stuff and Sid's grandpa, a medical doctor, insisted Sid should also be a doctor. After all, he was paying the bill.

My interest in math and science took off in an exponential manner. There were two books I had bought for kicks that had sat on the shelf at home. I started to read them in high school but got mired down in the weird looking math so I stopped. One was *Experiment and Theory in Physics*, by Max Born. The other was *The Principle of Relativity*, by Einstein, Lorentz, Weyl and Minkowski.

I showed my physics professor the two books I had and explained I was having difficulty understanding much of it. I told him I was following some of the integral and differential equations based on what I was picking up in calculus.

He sort of laughed and said, "You have a long way to go in advanced math yet." He was a short man with long, thin, gray hair. All I knew was he had studied in Germany. As he sat behind his desk covered with papers and books he thumbed through the book on relativity all the time playing with his mustache. He asked if I was getting anything out of what I was reading. I told him it was very interesting about how light-rays would bend around a gravitational field, but when I got to the contra-variant symmetrical tensor and energy-density tensor discussion, I was lost.

"Well," he said, "They have proven by experiment that light-rays appear to bend around a strong gravitational field. This is due to the gravity curving the surrounding space. As to whether gravitational waves exist as the theory proposes is yet to be proven. I'm sure we will know more as we study the behavior of hydrogen," he went on.

"Hydrogen? I don't get it," I frowned.

"Yes go to references on work done by Rabi and Lamb. They and others before them, like Niels Bohr, had studied the energy states of hydrogen. The hydrogen atom is very unique but its simplicity is the key to actually understanding and justifying physical theories of the universe."

"Wow!" was all I could say, hardly wanting to wait until my senior courses in physics.

I always found it amazing how scientists distill the complex makeup of nature into a simple concept or formula to describe a relationship. These same scientists are also found to touch on the concept of the Deity. The relationship of matter and its ultimate energy conversion equivalent is shown by Einstein in his famous equation $e=mc^2$. In his early expressions he used to put the Greek symbol lambda (λ) in the equation. It did nothing, as it had no units of measure, but it stood for "The Old One" the way he recalled God. By the way, do you have any idea what $e=mc^2$ means? Well you know what a dime is. If you convert the mass of a dime to energy, the result would be equivalent to 670,000 gallons of gasoline!

Scientists think the universe has another dimension beyond our three spatial and the forth dimension of time. I wonder if this fifth dimension, which we apparently can only detect by indirect methods, Einstein would call lambda hydrogen. Good for a laugh from the technical readers.

I bought a ledger and started to record names and references of what I was picking up in discussions with my teachers and other sources. It was handy to work with. While at the library, I could briefly document reference material and a source to work from to prepare term papers. The ledger became my journal of thoughts and notes. I also jotted down comments and ideas to check on at a later time.

At summer break I looked for a job. Dad knew the head of the US Forest Service that oversaw the engineering office, so he took me by to meet him. He in turn took me to see John Stentz the project engineer. I think he felt a little under pressure but took the steps to get me hired. Little did I realize it was the beginning of my government service. The job was interesting. I was in the field part time with the survey crew and then in the office laying out the data from the field excursions. Both Stentz and the survey crew took the time to show me the ropes of the trade. Stentz was short, thin, man with blond hair who had a master's degree in civil engineering. When he needed me from the field he would ask for the "budding physicist."

Towards the end of the summer, Stentz called me and the crew in.

"Got a project for you guys called 'Lost Johnny'," he said.

Lost Johnny was a stream that fed into the South Fork of the Flathead River on the west side of the Hungry Horse dam reservoir, just south of Glacier National Park.

"Since Bain is leaving us in a few months to go back to Bozeman, I want you guys to really put some responsibility on him, maybe we can make a civil engineer out of him!" He chuckled, as though I might change my academic pursuit.

The guys did as they were told. We spent two weeks camped out in the Lost Johnny drainage laying out different grade lines to determine the best option to put in a road. Back at the office we used the survey information to draft the drawings and specs. Several times a week I went with Stentz out to the site to monitor the construction progress. He showed me how they determine where to locate the culverts under the road and how to size them according to the water runoff data they had documented over the years. I was, in fact, getting very interested in civil engineering.

Not far up the main road from Lost Johnny road are the Twin Creeks. So, needless to say, when I go to Montana and go fishing it is nostalgic to take a quick run up to Lost Johnny and reminisce.

* * *

In the fall of 1955 I started my junior year and was back at the Hudson House.

I enrolled in the Air Force Reserve Officers Training Corps offered by the college. I really liked the program because we studied aerodynamics, atmospheric phenomena, and related topics about aircraft design and operations. I was always asking questions about rockets but the instructors were of no help.

Major Stone, one of my instructors was aware of the German rocket activity during the war and thought their operations had moved to the US. He put me in touch with a source that indicated there was a rocket program in New Mexico and Texas. Apparently there had been a project called "paperclip" in which the German scientist, von Braun, and his team were brought to the US.

One day during a lecture on aircraft engines I asked Major Stone, "Why not use hydrogen as a fuel in the jets?"

He replied, "Are you nuts, Bain, ever hear of the Hindenburg?"

The class laughed at me. I took it in stride. At the time I knew little about the *Hindenburg* disaster.

The next day Major Stone called me to the side just before class started. He was a small man with the typical flattop crew cut and starched uniform.

"Bain, sorry about throwing cold water on your hydrogen idea," he said apologetically. "You might check some things the Germans were doing back in the 30's. They knew a lot about hydrogen because of its use in airships. I also read something about using it to power a bus. Look up the name Erren. The Air Force, I understand, has considered hydrogen off and on as an aviation fuel. The idea dates back at the turn of the century."

These ideas would have more significance later in my life. I made sure I jotted them down in my ledger.

* * *

At the end of the first quarter of my junior year at college, I headed home to Kalispell for Christmas break. I was running low on money.

I had to find a job but didn't want to give up pursuing my education. A friend had mentioned some of the programs the military had to offer, and the Service started to sound like a decent compromise. I could go to school, have a job, an income and lodgings, all in one. I sat down with Mom and Dad to tell them what I was contemplating.

"My first choice, if I can get it, is a job in the Air Force. At least then I can be around airplanes."

"But, what if they're not accepting new recruits right now?" Mom replied.

"Well, then I'll try the other branches of the Service."

So, off I rambled in my cream colored, two-door '51 Ford, smack-dab into a frigid Montana winter. My first stop was the Air Force recruiter in Butte, Montana. With no luck there, I tried the Navy, then the Army, and soon thereafter I found myself knocking on the door of my last resort—the Marines. The response was unanimous. Mom was right.

Downhearted, but still determined, I began to ponder my alternatives. All of a sudden, I remembered my friend Sid. He had a knack for finding good jobs and was working in Trout Creek on the Noxon Rapids Dam project. They were constructing a mile-long dam across the Clark Fork River near a site called Noxon Rapids. The Washington Water Power Company was the financier for the project and a company called Ebasco was running it.

Back then Trout Creek was barely a wide spot in the road with only a gas station and a bar. The closest lodging was a hotel forty miles away in Thompson Falls. That was where Sid was staying, so I cruised over in the Ford but didn't arrive until long after dark. That meant I would have to sleep in the car. I was overjoyed when the sun came up and I could catch up with Sid. He told me to see Dick Ensign the Resident Engineer at Ebasco. He was looking for draftsmen, especially guys with civil and mechanical experience.

During the next three years, Dick and his engineering staff did much to help me learn the trade. That included architectural, civil, electrical, structural, and mechanical detailing, among other things. Dick had a master's degree in hydraulics and guided me through such topics as spillway crest design, abutment erosions, and river-flow calculations. Jim was well versed in civil engineering and taught me about free haul, mass diagramming, retaining walls, embankments, bridge work and highway relocation designs. Determined to use my math education, I developed a new analytical method of determining the volumes of irregular structures specific to the project. This process was a method to calculate such things as volumes of soil removed, or placement of various clays and rock used in construction, and the placement of concrete. The Morrison-Knudsen Company, primary contractor for the Noxon Dam project, used it to figure contract pay-quantities. Each month, we had to do runs to stay up with the progress of the project.

* * *

I set up my ten-wide house trailer on a tiny lot across from the Noxon Hotel. I added on a room to serve as my workshop, and I began repairing radios and TV's to pick up extra money for college. I built most of the test equipment from Heath Kits that contained all the parts and assembly instructions needed for a vacuum tube tester, oscilloscope, frequency analyzer, and so forth. With the help of the area's one and only electronics repairman within 50 miles, my new little side business did well.

One evening, October 4, 1957, to be exact, I was listening to the radio. Just then, exciting news came in over the airwaves. A satellite had been launched into space for the first time. This was truly an historic moment. I hurried to my workshop and spent the rest of the night listening to the "beep, beep, beep," which was broadcast, every ninety-five minutes, from my short wave Halicrafter radio.

Wow, they finally did it! I thought. They succeeded in sending a satellite into orbit around the earth.

Yes, it was exciting, yet on the other hand, quite shocking. The Russians had succeeded first, a fact not only disappointing, but also disturbing.

The Sputnik news set everyone at work abuzz, especially Jim. He and I often talked about rockets, satellites, and the universe when we went fishing together. We'd sit on the bank, lines in the water, while I rattled on for hours about going into space. Jim was twenty-five years my senior and very sharp witted.

At lunchtime we were all gathered around the table discussing the exciting news of the Sputnik.

"You know guys, satellites will probably be used to develop a worldwide communications system and will most likely find military applications too. A nation in control of space will be a nation in control of the planet," I declared.

They all gawked at me, eyes wide with disbelief. You could have heard a pin drop. Jim cracked a wide smile and then turned around and proceeded outside. I followed, soon after, and found him with his tall, slim torso leaned against the lunchroom wall. He was staring at the sky, arms tightly crossed over his chest and a cigarette dangling from his lower lip. I could see that he was in deep contemplation.

"Hey there, buddy," he said, as he came back to earth.

A small cloud of smoke rose above his head as he took a final drag off his hand-rolled Bull Durham.

"You know, Addison, you really scared the hell out of us in there! So, tell us, what's gonna happen next?" he asked, as though I were psychic.

"Well, I imagine that this will be another wake-up call for the US, just like Pearl Harbor was, but it's always hard to tell what the politicians and four-stars will do," I shrugged.

"No, no…I mean those damn Ruskies. What are *they* gonna do?"

"Oh, them…. well, I don't know, Jim. Maybe they'll put a woman into orbit, " I teased.

"Right," he smirked. He shook his head and rolled another Bull Durham.

"I bet von Braun could put up a satellite in no time," I half mumbled to myself.

The dam project was coming to an end so one of my first tasks was to arrange the sale of the trailer. I then moved into the Noxon Hotel and found a room with a closet large enough to store my electronic gear, my books and my cherished jet engine model airplane. With the money I anticipated from the sale of the trailer, my dream of going back to school was nearing reality.

* * *

Shortly after settling in Noxon, I had joined the American Rocket Society (ARS) and the British Interplanetary Society, and received their publications on a regular basis. Noxon didn't have a library, so I had to jot down notes in my journal and planned to do my research later in Bozeman. In the 1958 summer edition of the ARS Journal, I spotted an announcement about an ARS conference that was going to be held in Los Angeles.

The conference was well attended that first day, and most of the papers presented were highly technical. Several of them really intrigued me, and I began to realize that I was lagging far behind in the latest rocket technologies.

After dinner, cocktails were made available at an open bar on the other side of the room. The air was alive with discussion as people claimed their drinks and casually gathered into small groups. In one of the clusters, I spotted a familiar face. It was George Sutton, author of *Rocket Propulsion Elements*. I had purchased his book during registration and recognized him from his photo on the back cover. After carefully checking my cash supply, and with my ARS member discount, I figured I could afford to buy his and two other titles: *Rocket Missile Propulsion*, published by Rocketdyne, and a newer version of a copy that I owned of Willy Ley's *Rockets, Missiles & Space Travel*. A true rocket fanatic, I could never resist such titles.

As I timidly joined the group, someone squinted down at my nametag and said, "Addison Bain, I would like to introduce you to George Sutton."

Feeling ambushed, all I could say was, "Hi, I just bought your book and I'm really looking forward to reading it tonight."

"It will put you to sleep," he said, and the group burst into laughter.

With the day's activities over, I returned to my hotel room at the Convention Center. Picking up Sutton's book, I intended to read a few chapters but became so absorbed that I traded off sleep to read much of it. Certain elements of the book played in my mind, specifically the subject of hydrogen, and it struck me then that hydrogen has great specific impulse characteristics. The notion was tantalizing! As sleep finally came, I promised myself I would find Sutton the next day and ask him more about it.

It was my lucky day. I spotted Sutton eating alone at a table by the window.

"Good morning Mr. Sutton," I said.

"I just wanted to say that I really enjoyed your book and it didn't put me to sleep at all. In fact, it got me thinking about some things. If you have a few minutes, would you mind if I asked you a couple of questions?"

"In your book, you spoke of hydrogen and I found it intriguing. All I know about it is that it's cold and flammable, but maybe it has potential for rocket propulsion. What are your thoughts on that, sir?" I prodded enthusiastically.

"Personally, I think it has excellent possibilities, but a lot of my colleagues don't like it; von Braun for example. Ever since 1937, the Germans have seriously questioned using it, but there are some fellows at an aeronautical facility in Cleveland who are looking into using liquid hydrogen as an upper stage rocket engine fuel. Look into some reports by the National Advisory Committee for Aeronautics."

Sutton then dropped the subject, but continued to rattle on about rocket engines. His knowledge, and how thoroughly he knew the business, was astonishing. Time was short, so I didn't get a chance to talk to him about Willy Ley's discussion on hydrogen in his book. Ley had indicated, "Hydrogen has a number of features which are, to say the least, annoying." He went on to suggest that it would be unlikely that hydrogen would be used in its pure form as a rocket fuel. This point intrigued me and I hoped for an explanation from Sutton.

Looking at his watch, he leapt from his chair, grabbed my hand, and shook it. "Must go now, nice meeting you," he blurted.

I thought back to Sutton's comment about the year 1937.

"Wasn't that the year the *Hindenburg* burned?" I pondered. I made a mental note to look it up as soon as I got home.

A man by the name of Krafft Ehricke was also at the conference. I was disappointed in not meeting him. Years later I found out that he headed up the development of the first US rocket engine to run on hydrogen. The engine was used for the Centaur vehicle.

The conference included a trip to "Susy", an engine test facility in the Santa Susana Mountains. During the 45-minute bus journey up to the test site, I overheard some of the people complaining about the winding mountain road.

"A piece of cake compared to the mountain roads of Montana," I chuckled to myself.

The bus finally rolled to a stop and just as I descended the steps, a loud rumble roared out from the mountainside. An enormous white plume of smoke billowed up against the blue California sky and I blurted, "Wow, they're firing a rocket engine!"

"That's a gas generator," the man behind me remarked snidely.

I think he was trying to imply that I was sadly misinformed, but I was too charged with adrenaline to let it bother me. My goal was to gather as much information on this trip as I could. I soon learned that the gas generator was the device used to propel the liquid fuel pumps on a main rocket engine.

Later that day, there was a special engine firing demonstration held for the group, the kind eventually used for Atlas ballistic missiles. For me, that was the icing on the cake.

The conference came to a close the following morning, and I took the flight back to the Spokane Airport. Retrieving my car, I headed to Noxon. It was already late at night when I crossed over the narrow bridge into town. I took the path that went around to the back of the hotel. After business hours, they always locked the front entrance, but I had a key that would let me in through the back door.

Only a tiny sliver of moon hung in the murky heavens that night. The sky, too opaque for shadows, shed an ominous mood over the landscape. I quietly rolled to a stop and turned on the high beams to help me find the entryway. However, the lights only shined out into a black void, beams unhindered by the door or any other object. My stomach began to churn.

Nausea rose and caught in my throat. Reluctantly, I opened the car's door and stepped out, trying to orient myself in the dark. Headlights still blazing, I found no door! Moreover, no hotel either, only a thick gloom and the faint smell of smoke lingering in the chilly night air.

Now homeless, I knew Jim would take me in, regardless of the late hour. He was that kind of a guy. I started the engine and looked behind me before putting the car in reverse. There, on the back seat, I noticed my suitcase. Inside, there were three books, the conference proceedings and a few dirty clothes. That was all that remained of my worldly possessions.

The following day, I went back to view the remains of the hotel. I stood staring at the spot where my room had once been. All that remained were ashes… nothing but ashes. I figured that it must have been a very hot fire as even the titanium fuselage of my model airplane had melted. My mahogany boat was recognizable only from the charred jet engine. All of my books were gone, even the very rare math book that Sid's grandpa gave me. I saw no evidence, however, of my electronic gear.

"Hmm, that's odd," I thought, scratching my head.

Suddenly, I remembered my journal.

"Oh God, please, not my journal," I moaned to myself.

I picked up a charred tree branch from the ground and poked around through the ashes and debris but no luck.

Traumatized by all that had happened, I decided a good, cold mug of beer was in order, so I headed for the town's most popular saloon, Little Red's. The place was named for the owner, a feisty, sexy little redhead. Petite, she was, but she packed a heavyweight repertoire of swear words potent enough to keep those good ole "dam" boys in their place if they got too rowdy. In addition to the beer, I figured I might also be able to tap into some of the local secrets. This was the best place in town to find out what was going on, and I needed to track down the owners of the hotel.

When I finally caught up with them, I discovered that they had kindly rescued some of my electronic gear, things they said they believed were the most important, as they later explained. "Why most important?" I wondered. There were some strange things going on, and they seemed to get stranger by the minute.

At that point, I decided it would be a good idea to go pay a visit to the "friends" who had bought my trailer, but when I glanced across the street, lo and behold, the trailer was gone! It had disappeared, along with all the unmade payments I was counting on. I had received only the first few.

Eventually, I learned from the locals that the hotel no longer had enough clients to remain in business. Many workers were being laid off from the dam project. The friends in my trailer had skipped town, and I was not the only one they'd left high and dry. I tell this story for the younger generation, because life's events can sometimes unexpectedly take away your physical assets, but you will still have your knowledge.

Jim and his wife let me stay as long as possible, but the day came when I needed to find a new place to hang my hat. They recommended I go see their friend, Stella. She had a big ranch house and rented out rooms to local laborers. Luckily, she agreed to take me in. The thought of having my own space again was wonderful.

I checked my mailbox at the post office every other week or so. Then one day I turned the key in the mailbox lock, pulled open the door and drew out a small stack of envelopes. There were the usual ads, a newsletter from the ARS, and a letter from the Selective Service System.

"What? The Selective Service!"

I dropped the rest of my mail to the floor and ripped open the envelope in a blind panic. I squinched my eyes tight, hoping that when I opened them, I'd find this was just a dream and not the nightmare that I was beginning to imagine. Taking a deep breath, I opened my eyes, unfolded the letter and read…

"Mr. Addison Bain, Greetings from the President of the United States. You are hereby ordered to report to the US Army Induction Center in Butte, Montana, February 2, 1959."

Before my eyes, my mailbox turned into Pandora's box and released an evil thing in the form of a piece of paper. This thing had the power to turn me into a ground-hugger. In a few weeks, my very being would be transformed.

But being drafted into the Army turned out to be the first step on the way to my dream…working with rockets and an ensuing career with NASA.

Chapter 2

Rockets and Missile Fuels

I reported to Fort Ord California the end of February 1959, via train from Kalispell. The first eight weeks was the program of "basic training" as they called it, to make soldiers out of us to be ready to go somewhere and kill people. Me? Yeah right!

Basic training was part fun and part hard work. Getting up before dawn and running five miles or more was work for a lot of us, and so were the gut-busting calisthenics, calisthenics and more calisthenics! Getting screamed at by a drill sergeant with his mouth six inches in front of my face was something new. We eventually learned how to disassemble the M1 rifle blindfolded. Then the sergeant would rearrange the parts on the table and we had to reassemble the rifle, all in less than one minute. Shooting the 50-caliber machine gun was fun, but the most fun of all was the bazooka. The objective was to hit an old armored tank a few hundred yards away with the rocket shell. The temptation got to me, and of course I got into trouble by firing it up at a 45-degree angle.

"But Lieutenant, that is how you get the most range," I responded to his nasty comment that I was doing it wrong. We were run through a tear gas chamber to learn how to use a gas mask. Then we had to remove the mask and go for the exit door. Needless to say most of us wound up on the ground coughing, choking and carrying on.

Looking back I would say "basic training" is an experience every man should go through. You learn discipline, respect and how to work together. As part of the honor guard I found it more so.

In eight weeks many of my buddies were assigned to go to Germany, the rest to other parts of the world. I waited and waited for orders. Then one day the Captain called me in.

"Private Bain, we want two years from you. We can give you two choices as to what we can do for you."

Without hesitation I said, "I want something to do with rockets, that's it." At the time I knew the Army had rocket stuff going on in New Mexico. A few days later I got my orders to report to Redstone Arsenal, Alabama.

"Redstone Arsenal," I pondered, "What the hell is going on there?" Anyhow, I was able to go home for a few weeks to tell the folks.

*   *   *

I took the train to Huntsville, Alabama.

It was May 1959, I was walking up the steps to the headquarters building 4488 at the Army Ballistic Missile Agency (ABMA), Redstone Arsenal, Alabama (sixteen months later President Eisenhower renamed it the Marshall Space Flight Center). Coming down the steps were General Medaris and Dr. Werner von Braun. Dr. von Braun! The name I had followed ever since Major Stone's class at Bozeman! My heart stopped. They were to be my bosses, many tiers up of course. Von Braun glanced down to see my nametag on the drab, yet freshly starched Army green uniform sporting the Private stripe on each sleeve. Another clue to his sharp, observant eye was the manila folder in my hand containing my orders to report.

"Private Bain," he said, "Which lab are you reporting to?" Except for a few administrative buildings, the place was sprawling with labs.

"Well sir, I don't know yet until I get to Personnel," I trembled, "I have been assigned the position of physicist."

"You 'vill' probably be assigned to the G&C Lab," he said with a smile and slight Austrian accent. He and Medaris continued on in an apparent rush.

"Good luck," he said as he glanced back.

He was right, Personnel had openings in the Guidance and Control (G&C) Laboratory.

I could not wait to get back to the barracks that night to call the folks in Kalispell. With a voice of tears and excitement, I told Mom and Dad about the events of the day.

I was on cloud nine. I was into the real rockets! I was under an experimental program that the Army had. It was called the Scientific and Engineering (S&E) program, made up of guys with college backgrounds. The idea being that we needed to serve our time under the draft, but why not take advantage of the education we had.

The S&E program allowed us to select locations at ABMA as we wished. I spent most of my time in G&C, but later spent some time at the materials testing lab and wind tunnel.

I worked with a couple of Ph.D.'s on a secret project to work out a problem with launch impact accuracy. Apparently, the Redstone rocket was not hitting on target. We found that the on-board computer needed to adjust for gravity changes during flight. We "published" our study on the Gravity Feedback Equations. It was later used on the Saturn vehicle as well. Then

I was trained to calibrate the gyro accelerometers used on the instrument rack of the rockets before the rack was shipped to Cape Canaveral, Florida, commonly referred to as just *the Cape*. The three accelerometers, each oriented to one of their three spatial dimensions, would send signals to the on-board computer letting it know the position of the rocket in flight.

The assignment at G&C was unforgettable. I was working on secret stuff and was reminded of it everywhere I looked. Of course I had to have a clearance badge to get in the lab areas. At the fenced-in area around G&C there was first a guard at the gate to assure I was assigned to the lab. Then there was a backup guard inside the lobby to double-check my ID. Then down one wing where the Advanced Guidance office was located, there was a guard stationed at a desk to greet each person.

Much of the guidance equations were similar, but the role of the office was to improve them or develop what was needed for changing missions. Each page of a report was stamped in bold red letters at the top and bottom of the page, "SECRET."

At the end of the day everything was to be put in special file vaults and recorded and countersigned. The reverse process occurred every morning. Since a lot of the reports in process had boilerplate information in them, the guys would cut off the "secret" labels, and put them into the shredder. They did this to save the hassle of putting draft reports into the vaults, recording them, and countersigning them.

I learned to use the many types of computers. From the hard-wire Burroughs 101 to the vacuum tube Datatron 250. Then IBM came out with the fancy high-speed computer that used tiny magnetic coils in a cross-matrix. The massive units took up rooms of space. My home computer today can run circles around those older machines—amazing!

Another assignment was in the wind tunnel. We found that the typical pointed nose cone of the rocket was not the optimum configuration. It would easily burn up from the friction of the air caused by traveling at high rates of speed. A parabolic shape proved a better design, something to do with the ratio of surface area and the mass of the cone. It was my first real opportunity to apply my college thermodynamics studies. The guys in the lab helped me with the calculations on heat transfer and to learn about the resistance of the various materials with high temperatures.

* * *

My army friend Dean had a '56 Ford that we converted to run on propane. This was my first experience in setting up a car to run on an alternative fuel. The large tank in the trunk made it rear-end heavy and obvious to the observer. We were stopped by the police several times as a potential booze runner. I recall the one time we raised the trunk lid and told the officer to place his nose near the vent pipe. Dean turned on the vent valve and the officer got a face full of propane gas, expecting moonshine (something they look for in the South). I thought for sure we were going to jail.

Huntsville was a boring place for a number of college guys in the Scientific and Engineering group. So we formed a fraternity called the Phi Tau Alpha. Many of the guys could not cope with doing KP (kitchen patrol), marching, and other Army stuff that we had to do in parallel with the "job" we had. I remember one Ph.D. who was a private. He told me about the time he had a meeting with some executives from Rocketdyne. They made good money and he made $78 a month like the rest of us.

There were 35 of us. We each chipped in $5 a month and rented a large house and built a 15 foot long bar and fixed up the four bedrooms upstairs and the rooms on the first floor of the mansion on 516 Franklin Street. I set up all my electronic gear that I had at Noxon in one of the upstairs rooms. Some of the other guys had equipment as well so we had our own little lab. The house was not only a place to get away from the arsenal but a place to get together and talk about our on hands-on experiences with rockets and what we were going to do after we got out of the Army. And of course, the "frat" was a place to have an occasional party.

*   *   *

I bought another ledger and started a new journal on my thoughts and technical references. They had a good library on the base I could use. Of course I could get almost anything on rockets and space that was not classified. I tried to recall some of the reference stuff I lost at Noxon in the fire, but I basically was starting from scratch. There were a lot of references to the hydrogen rocket fuel concepts with experiments conducted at Ohio State University and the Jet Propulsion Lab at Cal Tech in Pasadena, California.

I joined the local hot rod club at the time. The Rebels— a fitting name for the South. I justified my membership by claiming that since I was from Montana, I was really not a Yankee, so it was okay. I told them of my work on hot rods in Montana and Alabama. In 1960, I drove my '53 Packard to Huntsville. With the help of the club we dropped in a souped-up, late-model, Olds engine. The engine was a lot shorter than the straight eight we removed, so we needed longer water hoses. After looking around the salvage yard at the space center, we came up with some titanium piping. The lab also built me a special battery box to hold the two 12-volt batteries along with a starter switch and some other goodies made of shiny stainless steel. For example, the air inlet to the carburetors looked like something out of "Star Wars," with its corrugated titanium scoops, once used as fuel feed lines on the Redstone rocket engine. On a trip back home Dad lifted the hood.

He exclaimed, "Holy cow! A rocket engine!"

We used to go to Guntersville where there was a quarter mile drag strip and run our cars. On one occasion, I met Evel Knievel. It was easy to spot his combed-back, wavy hair and his trademark black leathers. He was from Butte, Montana and I knew that. He had a Harley bike with the motorcycle engine replaced with a V-eight Chevy engine mounted crossways. What a weird sight. A couple of us helped push the bike to get the engine started and then pull it back to the starting line and get it up on the rear bike stand. It was obvious this daredevil knew what he was doing. It helped when I introduced myself as being from Kalispell. He did not permit just anybody touching his bike. Montana guys were okay.

He revved up the engine and watched the temperature gage. There was no radiator to cool the engine, but there was just enough "cooling" water in a piping assembly connected to the engine water jacket. When he nodded his head that meant the temperature was up so we pushed the bike off the stand. He left a black-purple swath on the tarmac and a trail of smoke, zigzagging all the way down the drag strip. I always wondered what speed he reached.

*　*　*

It was early 1961 when I got out of the Army as a "Spec 4", with an honorable discharge I might add, and spent some time back in Kalispell.

I then got a phone call from Brown Engineering in Huntsville offering me a job as a draftsman. Back to Alabama in the old Packard I went. "Will I get to work on rockets again, I wondered?" It started out great. I worked with the civil engineering guys designing a rocket engine test-stand where hydrogen fuel was to be used.

I stayed at the frat house since it only cost me five bucks a month. It was a great help to get back on my feet again while I looked around for an apartment.

* * *

Later in 1962, I was at a drafting table in what was known as the "Hick" building in downtown Huntsville, Alabama. The Hick building was an old converted cotton mill next to a defunct railroad in not a very nice part of town, but I didn't care. Brown Engineering was about to make me an expert in high-pressure gas and liquid forms of helium, nitrogen, oxygen, and hydrogen systems design.

Staring at the table, I knew I could draw and detail out what the assignment might be in terms of structures, but I knew little about missile fuels. I did understand some about hydrogen and oxygen, and purge gases like helium and nitrogen from the books I had again accumulated, but I knew it wasn't enough knowledge to give me the confidence I needed for my designs.

I, of course, got help from the engineers in the Pneumatics Branch where I was assigned. Doug, Tom, Charlie, Ed, Troy, Bill and Mark helped me with technical details and gave me the reference work to study in order to gain the knowledge I needed. I was grateful for their assistance. Doug gave me a text on *High Pressure Technology* by Comings to read, and the latest version of *Cryogenic Engineering* by R. B. Scott. I found out

Arthur D. Little, Inc. had done some work on hydrogen fuel for the Air Force, as did The Bureau of Standards in Boulder, Colorado.

The engineers would spell out the technical detail and calculations, and I would transform them into drawings and a set of specifications. It seemed we were all learning this new business at the same time. We had a flood of company reps in our office all the time pushing their wares. They marketed valves, connectors, piping and other components that made up the ground support equipment for the rocket programs. The equipment would be designed and later assembled at Cape Canaveral, Florida.

I went to the Cape in 1962 to visit the launch sites and watch John Glenn's flight. Wow! What an inspiration to be part of the space program. It was our boss, Charlie, who wanted all of us to go to the Cape now and then to see first hand what we were working on.

I enjoyed my work, but I needed to get back to school, so I enrolled in the local college night school and went into engineering and mathematics. The dream of being a nuclear scientist had faded and now I was preparing for a career in rocket engineering.

* * *

I continued working on cars on the weekends, mostly for the guys who still lived at the frat house. I remember the first Borg-Warner automatic transmission I tore apart to rebuild. It was for the Rebels. They were building a racing machine as cheaply as they could. The idea was to start out with the best of Detroit that we could find in a scrap yard, and then get the high-performance stuff like a full-race camshaft from a hot rod shop.

35

The Borg-Warner transmission had over 200 parts. That wasn't the bad news. I had them all on the kitchen table...*that* was the bad news! In my own defense, it was a little tough to work on cars without a garage, let alone a shop, especially in the winter when it was too cold to go out on the back porch where I did most of my work.

I kept in contact with Dad on this project since he was professionally trained in working on automatic transmissions—slush-o-matics, as we called them. He had already been briefed on how to modify the valve body, the clutch-plate assembly and vacuum controls to get a better shift pattern for racing configurations. The high-performance racing equipment put a strain on the transmission. The transmission had to be accurately reworked so it wouldn't come unglued on the drag strip. Fortunately I had a friend in Huntsville who owned a machine shop where I could use the shop equipment.

The Rebels used a variety of fuels. They were mostly high-octane gasoline with blends such as "nitro." I did recall Major Stone's reference to the hydrogen-fueled projects in Germany. The Rebels had a problem with that idea. I pointed to the acetylene tank that we used for welding, and tried to convince them that acetylene was a heck of a lot more dangerous than hydrogen.

Sometimes I worked on my own "racing cars." I really liked the '53 Studebaker Champion. At one time, I had four in the yard in various stages of "development" or just sitting as a source of spare parts. One had an engine, sporting two-carburetors, a roller-tappet camshaft and the latest in aluminum pistons. I also copied an idea for a high-speed version out of a car magazine. This version incorporated flow tubes within the body to channel air pressure from the front through to the rear to balance the aerodynamic pressures, thus reducing drag. On the drawing board it was supposed to be good for 200 mph.

But family thought it was silly and a waste of money tinkering with cars, so I didn't do as much of it as I would have liked. Whenever I did work on them though, I always learned something I didn't know before, like how to weld aluminum tubing with oxy-acetylene—a skill only appreciated by someone who has tried to do it. One has the tendency to wind up with a puddle of molten aluminum on the ground.

I was always willing to learn new things at work, too. Ed took me out to the lab at Marshall Space Flight Center to participate in the hydrogen embrittlement test program. Not much was known about the reported effects of high-pressure hydrogen on certain metals except that some metals would weaken or become brittle. In an attempt to find out more information about this process, Ed ran across some interesting facts in the scientific journals. For example, he learned that a very small amount of oxygen would inhibit the embrittlement reaction. We verified this in the lab. This was valuable information because we now knew not to select those materials for use in the high-purity hydrogen systems.

Although the final design for the Saturn rocket support systems would use hydrogen at 6,000-psig, we ran tests at 15,000-psig to try to speed up the embrittlement process. We concentrated only on the materials initially selected as candidates for use.

Ed and I often came up with ideas and recommendations for component improvement in the overall system design. Not much was known about hydrogen at high pressures in the volumes we would be dealing with. We were sort of inventing the system as we went along.

Due to all the work with Ed, they assigned part of the ground support system to me. I was to lay out the design for the 6,000-psig high-pressure hydrogen system and work with Doug to prepare the specifications for the liquid-to-gas hydrogen recharger system. These recharger systems are still operating at the Cape today.

* * *

Bill Creel, one of the other engineers from Huntsville who had helped me when I first got there, was now the Chief of Pneumatics at the Cape. Bill hinted he was interested in getting me to the Cape to work with him. One day I paid him a visit. As I strolled with him through the Converter Compressor Facility (CCF) at Complex 34/37, he told me this is where he wanted me to work. I wondered if I could be an operator of this equipment. I told Bill I would think about it.

Back at Marshall, the folks in the office next to me were working on liquid hydrogen system designs for the Cape. I got to know the guys and spent time with them since their stuff was related to what I was doing. At the same time, other people at the NASA Lewis Research Center in Cleveland, Ohio, and NASA Stennis Space Center in Mississippi, were designing hydrogen systems. We all worked closely with each other, and Air Products and Linde, the producers of hydrogen. It was a team effort.

In the office, I also worked close to Mark. We developed a set of charts for hydrogen on compressibility factors, density at high pressures, and other relationships not in the books—at least not in the units we wanted to work with. We worked closely with Jesse Hord in Boulder, Colorado—later a dear friend and colleague on all sorts of hydrogen topics. Jesse was with the National Bureau of Standards (NBS), a really nice guy.

Jesse and his team did a lot of research coming up with engineering design data for hydrogen. They eventually

NBS LH$_2$ Plant

published their work as a monograph (NBS 168). He took me on a tour of the NBS liquid hydrogen plant that had operated from 1955 to 1959. The plant had a modest output of almost one-half a ton per day. In a later visit to NBS I was shown hydrogen in a slush state, observing it through a quartz window of the slush generator. The stuff actually looks like a "slushie" from the local ice cream shop! There has been much interest over the years to produce hydrogen in a denser form for use in aircraft or rockets. The objective is to get more energy in the fuel tanks to reduce the overall weight. There are other densified hydrogen ideas since the slush is difficult to handle.

Although we were working primarily on the Saturn rocket to support the Apollo program project, von Braun kept his vision years ahead. A committee, headed by propellant planners at the Cape, was formed to look at what may be needed to support the next generation of rockets, code named, Nova. The Nova vehicles would be many times larger than the Saturn

V rocket and there were three mission objectives. A lunar support station, an orbiting space station and manned mars missions (MMM) were planned. According to a 1963 report the MMM was top priority. Clearly, this was von Braun's personal objective. The overall ten-year program included many planned convoy trips (three or more spacecraft per trip) to Mars. The first Nova launch was "scheduled" for 1973. Total program cost was estimated at two billion dollars. The committee worked on a plan to identify the requirements for a massive amount of propellants, like hydrogen, to support the Nova program and make recommendations on how to implement the plan. The use of sub-cooled liquid hydrogen (to increase the density) was under consideration. But because this would require a significant advancement in booster technology, plus adding risk to potential success of vehicle launches, the concept was abandoned.

Pan Am, the Cape support contractor responsible for commodities planning, released the committee report. The team had conceived of a liquid hydrogen production plant to be built on the shores of Banana River within the boundaries of Cape Canaveral. The plant would provide the necessary requirements for space vehicle launches. It would be a partial-oxidation process using naphtha as a feedstock.

Naphtha is a heavy, oily petroleum compound, shipped from South America by barge. Partial-oxidation was the process to strip the hydrogen molecules from the carbon molecules in the naphtha compound using steam and oxygen. The resulting hydrogen had impurities like soot and sulfur and had to be cleaned before it was liquefied. It was the cheapest option at the time. My boss then, Charlie, who was working with the committee, cautioned me that politics would play a role in the plant's approval.

Union Carbide LH2 Plant

"Don't hold your breath, Addison," he told me.

By 1964 Union Carbide built a liquid hydrogen plant in Sacramento. It was the largest (and still is) single train production process at sixty tons per day. It was built to develop and test the M-1 engines for the second stage of the Nova vehicle. The Nova program was cancelled. The plant was shut down in 1969 and eventually dismantled. The plant intended for the Cape was not approved. Charlie was right. I was disappointed.

One day, a call came in from the Cape. It was Bill Creel. He said I needed to get some temporary duty—TDY—for a few days and see some of the problems with the high-pressure systems at the CCF. This was a ploy to get me down there to discuss my transfer to the Cape permanently. I spent a few days with Creel and he told me that Chrysler Aerospace was preparing a proposal to bid on the ground support contract that would include operating the CCF. He convinced me to fill out an application.

I called Dad to tell him about the idea of moving to the Cape. It was the summer of 1964 and he suggested I come home for a few days, go fly-fishing and think about it.

"I have to show you a new type of fishing with very small dry flies," he said.

"So how small?" I asked.

"Size #24. They are about three-sixteenths of an inch long," he chuckled.

"You've got to be kidding!" I said. I could hardly see to tie a #14! I liked to use a #12 or #14. A #12 is a half-inch long. Dad said he used a small magnifying glass that he rigged up and tied long, thin leaders to them at the house before he went out. He read about it in a sport magazine. They called it midge fishing. A midge is actually a very small fly, usually smaller than a "20" fishhook.

The midge fishing intrigued me, so off I went to Montana. Dad and I went to our favorite spot, The Twins. Midge fishing was harder than regular fly-fishing. It wasn't easy getting a small fly into the spot you wanted. There was the added challenge of trying to see that small fly float down the stream! You almost had to guess where it was. The one that got away was a fourteen-inch East Bank Cutthroat. Gorgeous. I played it up next to my boots where I was standing in the water, and then it was gone…midge fly and all. Well! I guess I'm going back to my #12 Joe Hopper.

I decided to take the job at the Cape. I returned home to Huntsville and started packing for the move. Troy, one of my engineering buddies at work, knew I was making a good decision to work at the Cape. I remember his parting words:

"Remember! Get your butt back in school!"

"Yes sir!" I replied, "And I hope I can count on you guys in the office to help me if I get into trouble with some technical stuff at the Cape."

"You know better than to raise that as any problem, Add," he scolded.

I headed off to Florida with a high feeling of confidence and all my worldly goods… which wasn't much!

Chapter 3

My NASA Career

In the summer of 1964, I drove to Florida and set up a temporary home in a Cocoa Beach motel. I reported to my contractor boss at the Chrysler Aerospace office and he took me to see NASA boss, Bill Creel. Together, we took a tour of the pneumatics systems at Complex 34 and 37. The equipment layout of the Converter Compressor Facility (CCF) was exactly what we had on the drawings in Huntsville. All was nearly in place and supporting the high-pressure gas needs at both launch pads.

My job was unique because I was helping Chrysler on proposal hints for the upcoming contract award while I worked at the CCF. Mechanics Dale, Mac, and Richard taught me how to operate the liquid nitrogen pumps and helium compressors. Portable trailers were used to haul helium and nitrogen around the Cape to other users. Mac had built them from scratch using old searchlight trailer chassis' mounted with high-pressure bottles he found in a defunct missile silo. The bottles carried gas at 6,000-psig and were delivered to various sites at other complexes. Those sites were active in supporting projects such as the Mercury and Gemini missions. Mercury, the one-man program, was coming to a close while Gemini, the two-man program, was just beginning. The three-man crew with the Apollo program was destined to go to the moon.

In December of 1964, the ground support contract was awarded to the Bendix Corporation. That meant I was out of a job and with Christmas around the corner, the timing couldn't have been worse. I resigned myself to the situation and began to clear my affairs from my office when Creel walked in.

"Hi Add. I just stopped by to tell you that I'm truly disappointed that things turned out this way. I wanted you to supervise the pneumatics functions under Chrysler, but this new contract has put an end to that idea," he apologized.

He ran the palm of his hand across the top of his head. His hairline was rapidly retreating though he was barely 40, but vanity was not a part of Creel's character. His gesture told me that he had something else on his mind.

"Yeah, I'm sorry too, Bill. I really enjoyed my work here."

With a sly grin he continued, "Actually, there's another reason I wanted to see you today, Addison. How'd you like to join us at NASA?"

"Really?" I asked with suspicion. "That would be fantastic, but I doubt I could qualify. You know how impossible those procedures are under the Civil Service Recruitment Program," I sighed.

"Yes, I certainly do, and that's why we've come up with a new program called 'TAPER' to help us sidestep all of that. With this new procedure, we can hire people for a two-year probationary period. During that time, we will test their ability to perform and if they receive a satisfactory evaluation, the Civil Service System can accept them."

"Well, if that's the case, then count me in!" I said instantly.

He did, and on January 1, 1965, I became a GS-11 engineering tech working for Creel.

My new job at the CCF turned out to be more enjoyable than I'd ever imagined. Often, I'd go there alone on weekends and crank up the four Cosmodyne pumps to top off the nitrogen gas storage to 6,000-psig at the pads. However, the Cardair helium compressors at the other end of the CCF were another story. They didn't seem to put out like they should have. So, I set up a high-pressure bottle, measured the flow, and found that the units were not really designed for helium, but they worked well for compressing air. Over a period of time, I tinkered with them, made some modifications and they finally performed as required. The experience I gained working on engines and other automotive systems proved helpful.

One particular weekend, I went to the CCF to crank up the Cosmodyne pumps. While inspecting the gages on the control panel, I bent down to adjust the bypass bleed valve when, suddenly, an explosion rocked the area. Instinctively, I fell to the floor and covered my head. Quickly, but with caution, I looked up and saw that the panel was a mess and a white fog of nitrogen gas was spewing out and up. I lunged at the red emergency button and shut everything down.

With a closer look, I saw that the bourdon tube of the downstream pressure gage had ruptured and sent a quarter-sized piece of metal through the gage's faceplate.

When I turned around to see where it had landed, my skin erupted in goose bumps. Directly behind me, where I was standing before I hit the deck, was a hole in the wall that marked the impact point of the metal fragment.

"Thank God for instincts," I thought as I wiped my forehead. I roped off the area and headed home. En route, I took a detour and went by Bill's place to fill him in on what had happened. He offered me a drink and I didn't refuse. On the contrary, I said I'd take a bourbon and asked him to make it a double. My shattered nerves needed some serious soothing! We discussed the next steps. First, we implemented the "buddy system", that is, at least two people on any hazardous operation. Next, was to send out an alert. This went to industry and throughout NASA. It was recommended that for high-pressure systems, only gages having a solid front and a blow out back be used.

* * *

Creel always seemed to pick fights with "those design guys in Huntsville," as he liked to call them. He was an imposing figure and generally considered a bully. Fortunately, in my case, he took me under his wing and we developed a mutual respect. One particular day we were having a problem with the nitrogen system and Creel told me to call Huntsville and work it out with them. I pointed to the drawing signature block. Under "draftsman" were my glaring initials "ALB". He looked at me and said, "Fix it yourself!" We had a good laugh over the irony of it.

Those were also the days when everyone at the Cape helped each other, with or without formal approvals. Our motto was "get the job done." Debus, the first director of the Kennedy Space Center, requested that we look into the potential of hydrogen leaking into the Saturn V inter-compartments while they were under a nitrogen purge. He was concerned with the adequacy of the detection system. So, we set up a plenum, put it under a nitrogen flow and fed a measured amount of hydrogen into it so the instrument guys could calibrate their equipment.

"Careful with that hydrogen flow meter," Mac said. "I just borrowed it from the lab."

The words were barely out of his mouth when the glass front and venturi of the meter whizzed by my leg and shattered against the wall. Hydrogen began filling the area.

(It was a well-ventilated area and the flow of hydrogen was quickly shut off).

"Awe crap, Bain, how am I going to pay for that?" he moaned.

We'd been on the job that day for twelve hours, but we continued until the problem was solved. It was at that point that we realized we needed to regroup.

* * *

In those days, there was no OSHA (safety and health organization) to oversee the work environment, but we were supposed to don ear protection when the big birds flew from the pad, which was quite close to CCF 34/37. Nevertheless, I would step outside, push the ear pads off my head, sling them down around my neck, and bask in the thrusting rumble of those magnificent engines. The powerful vibrations ruffled my shirt like a blast from a Florida hurricane, and it felt glorious! I suspect the thundering decibels of those Saturn 1's, just nineteen hundred feet away, and the screeching of the compressors explains the tinnitus that plagues me to this day.

Saturn I liftoff

* * *

One day Creel told me I should join the Missile and Space Pioneer Club. That was the thing to do for the people working in the space program. So he sponsored me and I got with Joe Hilliard, the chairman of the club. After paying the lifetime fee he made arrangements for a certificate. He grandfathered me in, effective May 1959, when I first joined the missile team at Redstone Arsenal.

* * *

Our responsibilities included supplying the gaseous oxygen and hydrogen to the pad for space vehicle fuel cell support. At first, the commodities were delivered using "K" bottles, similar to the cylinders used for welding gases. However, the demands of the Saturn project would require the support of the oxygen and hydrogen storage containers and pumps then under construction and installation.

During that time I met Fred, the sales rep from Cosmodyne. He and Bud, the Cosmodyne engineer, had a skid-mounted liquid hydrogen pump flown in from California when it became apparent that the Linde rechargers we had on order would not be ready in time. We hooked up a 2,400-psig tube trailer to the recharger and then had the liquid supply tanker tied in. Next, we powered the recharger with a portable electric generator with a very long cord. The generator was not designed to be near hydrogen, so we modified the cord receptacle at the recharger end to make it explosion-proof. A flex line was attached to the bleed port, which was used for cooling down the recharger pump and the line ran down to the nearby ditch. There was the characteristic cloud at the end of the hose from the cold hydrogen gas as it condensed the water out of the air. As a precaution, we made sure that it was downwind and not near the generator. In a few hours, we had the tube trailer full. We disconnected and shut everything down and then headed off to Cocoa Beach. All the way there, Bud rambled on about how it was his dream to someday catch a sailfish.

In Cocoa Beach, our favorite watering hole was The Mouse Trap. They had excellent cocktails and the added perk of waitresses clad in scanty little mouse uniforms. Actually, they looked more like Playboy Bunnies than mice, but that suited us just fine!

By closing time, smooth-talking Bud had at least two girls ready to go deep-sea fishing with us the next day off the coast of Fort Lauderdale. I think the twenty-dollar bills he waved at them probably helped with the smoothing. We all worked hard and played hard, that was the way it was in the space program hay day.

* * *

In the summer of 1966, Debus got a call from NASA headquarters. The agency was beginning a collaborative effort with the Aerospace Data Research Institute to develop safety handbooks for propellants, and the first one was to be on hydrogen. They wanted a representative from each center and Lewis Research Center would take the lead. I was selected to represent KSC. Dr. Baulis and Paul Ordin at Lewis had already accumulated a lot of information on hydrogen from early Air Force studies, the Bureau of Standards in Boulder, and work done by the A.D. Little Company. Lewis had already done some jet engine and small rocket work using hydrogen.

Much data had been collected from the Centaur program. The Centaur was an upper-stage rocket using hydrogen fuel. The program started in the late 50's and the first Atlas / Centaur launch was in 1963. Of course, we already had a lot of information gathered from the efforts on the Apollo hydrogen projects. I had accumulated hydrogen information that was used to draw up the specs for buying hydrogen equipment and procedures used to operate them, along with material the hydrogen suppliers had given me. We also researched reports of hydrogen studies done in Russia through the Nuclear Energy Information Center and the Foreign Technology Division of the Department of Commerce. We concluded that Russia had used hydrogen as a fuel for the Sputnik mission. The Linde Division of Union Carbide was most helpful when I was working on hydrogen documentation in Huntsville.

We started an outline and took assignments to develop each section. Many drafts ensued. We made several trips to Lewis to help us produce a document we could be satisfied with. The *Hindenburg* topic surfaced frequently, but we chose to exclude it from our discussions. The work initially resulted in a hydrogen working-file whose chapters were arranged in a semi-orderly fashion. Finally, in 1968, the first edition of the *NASA Hydrogen Safety Handbook* was published.

Paul Ordin and I stayed in touch working on papers and attending hydrogen meetings together. He came up with the idea that a report should be put together that would list all the people engaged in various facets of hydrogen, sort of a who's who. This was started and eventually published in October 1975. It came out as a NASA document, *Registry of Hydrogen Experts* CR-2624. He also came up with a project to put together a report that listed accounts of hydrogen-related mishaps.

* * *

At Ryan Industries, three high-pressure gaseous trailers were slated for fabrication. One was for oxygen at 10,000-

psig, and two for hydrogen at 6,000-psig to support the Apollo program. However, I had a number of concerns. First, I needed to create a new Interstate Commerce Commission (ICC) spec, as the current 3A and 3AA ICC specs for cylinders would have restricted the design we wanted. Garland from ICC (now DOT), Van Vlack from US Steel, and myself met and created ICC spec 3AAX.

Once approved, US Steel began fabrication of the high-pressure cylinders for the trailer systems. Compatibility between the piping system connections to the cylinders and the control panel was also a concern. We tested many different materials. We burned up steel, stainless steel, aluminum, and the like, by flowing high-pressure oxygen through them. Finally, we discovered that Monel, a special steel alloy, was suitable. I created a Monel dip-tube design to place in the neck of the cylinder, which would eliminate any gas flow conditions across the carbon steel. The goal was to prevent erosion due to possible high gas flows across the steel surface that would in turn ignite the carbon steel. Early on, I was convinced that oxygen, what we breathe, could be more hazardous than hydrogen. We knew what hydrogen could or could not do. It was clearly more predictable.

The hydrogen trailer vent manifold was a concern. If a safety burst-disc were to inadvertently rupture, there would surely be a fire. We experimented with it and a fire resulted nearly every time. There was enough energy release to ignite the hydrogen with the air in the vent pipe. However, if the pipe was long enough, it extinguished itself. We used high-speed photography to study the problem. Normally the hydrogen flame is almost invisible, especially in daylight. But under the extreme flow rate, this short-lived blaze had a white, faint yellow glow. The scientists at the Cape thought this might be from the momentary combination of hydrogen with the nitrogen in the air to form a hydrazine radical that would take on this color while burning.

Hydrogen Compressed Gas Trailer

* * *

It was January 27th, 1967. I departed the CCF about 5:30 that afternoon to meet up with Fred at a party. A couple of hours into the merrymaking, someone entered the room with tears streaming down their face and announced, "the astronauts are dead!" Everyone was shocked and grief stricken.

Astronauts Grissom, White and Chaffee had burned to death in a flash fire in their capsule during a test countdown demonstration. The following day, the newspaper reported on the accident. "A spark, which ignited capsule material in the 100% oxygen used for a breathing atmosphere, was the apparent source of the catastrophe." At that moment, I was overwhelmed at how incredible it was that the very element, so indispensable to life, could so quickly take it away!

A few days later, Creel and his boss Gorman summoned me to their office. To their astonishment, a news reporter had published an article that claimed that the oxygen and hydrogen cylinders that we had set up for the test at the pad contributed to the accident.

"Add," Gorman said, "I want you to get with Bendix and track down everything you can find out… sample results, cylinder test reports, cleaning reports, everything! Get the picture? And, I want the results first thing in the morning," he insisted.

As requested I handed him a detailed report the next morning. We found no evidence linking the gas in the cylinders to the accident.

* * *

In the fall of 1967, I moved from the CCF 34/37 to the new CCF at Complex 39. This complex was designed to supply high-pressure gases to prepare for upcoming tests of the Saturn V, the gigantic moon rocket that would tower over 360 feet. The northeast corner of the CCF was exactly 11,800 feet from the center of the closest pad called Launch Pad 39A. We wanted the CCF to be as close to the pad as possible but not to resemble the concrete blockhouse buildings, a concept used on other launch pads. I calculated this distance while working on the CCF layout back in Huntsville. The building design had to conform to wind loads of a hurricane and be able to withstand the pressure wave of an on-pad explosion of a fully fueled Saturn V. Taking into account the energy of the hydrogen-oxygen fuel mix, and other on-board propellants, the pressure wave matched hurricane force at 11,800 feet. Kind of neat.

It was nighttime and a rainstorm was delaying the countdown of the Saturn V. My feet were propped up on the

CCF console, the headset hung loosely around my neck, and I was tuned in with our code name, GSPN, listening to the occasional chatter on the net. At the same time, I was studying for my final exam in Vector and Tensor Analysis.

Suddenly, Brad piped up, "Hey Add, let's go check on the hydrogen trucks."

So, off we went. Brad was the foreman in charge of propellant operations.

The liquid hydrogen tankers were parked just a little north of the CCF. Generally, the vent check valve kept roughly three pounds of pressure in the hydrogen tanker, but after an off-loading, some small venting of hydrogen would usually continue. Sometimes, there would be an almost invisible flame spurting out of the vent stack caused by static electricity being induced by an overhead cloud passage. This was not the norm but it occurred from time to time. It would ignite the hydrogen as it mixed with the outside air. We would simply open the main vent valve and snuff the flame out with hydrogen. With the fuel rich condition above the upper flammability limit of 75% hydrogen and 25% air, this was possible. Also, the cold hydrogen gas cooled down the vent hood. At the time, I thought it was awesome! A few years later the tankers were modified to include a helium vent purge system. This made the safety guys happy.

* * *

When I moved to Florida, I immediately enrolled in the local engineering college and chose their curriculum in Space Technology. I continued night classes for four years.

Chuck Copeland, a soft-spoken man from Pratt & Whitney, a company in West Palm Beach, was working on the RL-10 rocket engine program. One morning, he called asking for some hydrogen information as he'd heard about our novel hydrogen recharger. Built by Linde, it would pump liquid hydrogen to 6,000-psig, and vaporize it to provide the pressure and flow required to fill the gaseous hydrogen storage tanks. What was novel about the pump on the recharger was that it was submerged in the liquid phase of the tank. This kept it cold and prevented cavitation. Cavitation is when bubbles are formed in the liquid if the machinery is not properly chilled. As the bubbles collapse they can damage the metal parts of the pump. It was fun operating the Linde, it was easier to hook up and run than the skid mounted unit we had been using.

As fate would have it, twenty years later, I would marry Chuck's niece, Sharon.

* * *

The job of buying equipment to support the Apollo Program was seldom a piece of cake. After I completed the specifications for some high-pressure mobile rechargers, I realized how involved it was to get a contract for building equipment. I had to obtain seventeen signatures before procurement. Under pressure from Creel, I was obligated to hand-carry the request to expedite the process. We were asking for five units but only two tractors to couple with them. We thought we'd be able to use electrical shore power to operate them, or electrically power them from the tractor-mounted, Diesel engine alternators. It was a novel design.

I got along with everyone on our team with the exception of Rich. He was Creel's electrical engineer. Rich and I couldn't see eye to eye on many things. He was way behind in arranging for the electrical shore power that was needed for the program.

Unfortunately, it was my responsibility to obtain the crucial funding approval. That meant I was duty-bound to go through Pat in the Program Office for procurement, a step that no one relished. Pat's reputation preceded her and her petite stature belied her imposing character. She was brusque, by the book, and never known to crack a smile. In short, she was very intimidating.

I knocked on her open office door. I entered her office, introduced myself, and handed her the request package.

"Yes, yes, I know who you are and that you work in propellants. All you engineers think we have unlimited money," she huffed. "Sit down while I read through your proposal."

I nodded and sat down. As I waited, I made a mental tour of her office. There were no stacks of paper on her desk, yet she was responsible for processing hundreds of requests and keeping them all in order. What a contrast to the desk of an engineer, I thought. Everything in the room was neat and orderly.

"You know, Mr. Bain," her voice suddenly shook me to reality. "I wonder why you are buying five pumper units and only two tractors?"

I knew I had to think fast. I took a deep breath, found my voice, and seized the opportunity that had unexpectedly presented itself. Now, I can't even remember how I justified our request, but it apparently made sense to her. Pat wrote out and handed me an authorization that led to the construction of five Paul Chemical rechargers, five units and five trucks.

Not long after that Creel had Rich transferred elsewhere.

The Paul rechargers were nearing completion and chief engineer, Lloyd, requested I go out to the plant in Irvine, south of Los Angeles, to witness the acceptance tests. The contract required flow and pressure checks to insure compliance with the specs. During negotiation of the contract, the company had taken exception to doing the oxygen test run up to only 5,000-psig although the unit was "designed" for 10,000-psig. They were leery about going above 5,000-psig, as no one in the industry had done that yet at the higher flow rates.

I still recall the morning Lloyd picked me up at the motel to go to the test site. We stopped at a café to have a quick breakfast. We sat there looking at each other over a cup of coffee, but did not order. We both knew the recharger was filled with liquid oxygen and ready for the test. The company had made him move the unit about 250 feet out in a field away from the plant, just in case. Lloyd pulled out a flask of Jim Beam and proceeded to sweeten our coffee.

"You look like you need this too, Add," he said.

I didn't say much but he knew what I was thinking. The day before we had the techs retorque every fitting one more time. I went back over the cleaning certifications to verify that all the plumbing was super clean. Liquid oxygen, and especially very high-pressure oxygen is something to respect. A small amount of contamination, especially a hydrocarbon, like oil, is enough to make a nice bomb. Hell of a lot more hazardous than hydrogen. I had seen what the explosive nature of oxygen could do.

I had been on the investigative board involving an accident at the Brooklyn hospital. A 4,000-gallon liquid oxygen tank truck exploded killing the drivers and some hospital personnel. We also had a number of fires with oxygen at NASA. I was a little nervous to say the least.

Lloyd started up the pump. My position was at the rear control panel to monitor the output flow and pressure. I had already put a Monel fitting in the vent pipe several feet upstream of the gas exit point.

"Lloyd, if the steel pipe starts to glow, the fitting should slow down the process and give me time to holler to shut her down," I said with reservation.

"Add, I'm reading 5,000 on the pump gage. That was our limit."

"No, no you need that at the exit," I retorted.

He sheepishly looked around the corner of the unit and saw his boss and most of the workers standing in the large open doorway of the plant observing the test.

"Ok. Hang on, here goes," as he throttled down the bypass valve to increase the main flow pressure.

He was a small man and always had this sort of mischievous grin. He always impressed me with how he understood electrical-mechanical machinery. Suddenly, I was reading 7,500-psig on my gage. I looked immediately at him.

He grinned at me, "Is that enough Add?"

I just grinned back at him, "Yeah, sure, shut the son-of-a-gun down."

We discussed the fact that we would have been a lot less nervous if we were running a hydrogen machine.

Of all the machines I was involved in with the design, the Paul's were my favorite. It was my first experience in driving an eighteen-wheeler. The tractor was built by Peterbilt and had a V-12 cylinder, 434 horsepower engine. The inside of the cab was as plush as a Cadillac. We needed the high-pressure oxygen equipment to support the moon mission.

The astronauts wore a pressure garment assembly suit while walking on the moon. The assembly had two oxygen sub systems. A portable life support system as part of the suit backpack supplied breathing oxygen. Another system consisted of two spherical bottles pressurized with 7,500-psig oxygen and provided up to thirty minutes of emergency backup oxygen, just in case the astronaut sprung a leak in his suit.

Paul Chemical recharger

* * *

Politics often played a significant role in our line of work. A good example of that comes to mind when I think of the surplus, high-pressure, tube bank trailers that were stored just south of the space center at Patrick Air Force Base. We needed more trailers to service increased demands of hydrogen and other gases at a number of facilities. I contacted our chief mechanic, Ray, and we went to the base with five tractors and drivers to pick up the trailers. I told Ray that we had permission to borrow the trailers. After we had removed 25 units, a call came down from Air Force Command to halt the process, but we had already finished.

The loan of these "assets," a popular military term, "had not been approved" contrary to a letter we had from Robbins AFB, the Air Force equipment management center. So, Creel's boss, Gorman, called me in to advise me that I was on hand-receipt for two million dollars' worth of government equipment.

"But Chief," I asked, "What better deal can you get?"

He grinned and shook his head. He knew I would resolve the problem. I banked on the old adage that "possession is nine tenths of the law" and we kept the stolen trailers.

At the Cape I met some of Dr. Wernher von Braun's German Team that I had not met in Huntsville.

V-2 propellant loading

Albert Zeiler was one of those team members and he worked for NASA as a propellant expert. We often socialized and exchanged memories of our mutual missile propellant experiences. One of my favorite stories of his was the time when, during a countdown, a liquid oxygen hose did not automatically disconnect from a Redstone Rocket about to be launched. Albert, who was actually a mechanic, got the okay from von Braun to take a ladder and a hacksaw out to the rocket and cut it off!

Before he passed on, he gave me his file of photos and drawings of the V-2 rocket facilities at Peenemunde, Germany, his former employment site. My favorite photo is one that shows the V-2 being loaded with liquid oxygen with the attending crew standing around in street clothes. NASA would never have allowed this. They would have limited the number of people in an operation and insisted they wear special coveralls and personnel safety equipment. I framed that photo and it still stands proudly in the den next to my self-made model rocket.

*　*　*

At the Cape, after the logistics infrastructure had been well established for the Apollo Program, we had a problematic situation with the Kennedy Space Center and the Air Force Complex. Both were nearby and each had its own service contract with separate contractors. This duplicated our services, and propellant support was a key issue. A review team was formed to study consolidation and recommend which agency could best manage the functions. I was instructed to explore the matter of equipment consolidation and staff cuts. Mac was to examine propellant cost comparisons between NASA and the Air Force.

At times, I found it humorous how decisions were made. Mac used the Air Force stock-fund pricing data as a base for his calculations. He concluded that the Shuttle Program propellant cost would be more expensive with the Air Force. This was a deciding factor in choosing NASA to manage the function. Concurrently, I looked at the cost of hydrogen, the primary propellant for the Shuttle. The Air Force cost was four dollars a pound compared with a dollar per pound that NASA was paying. No one on the consolidation committee noticed the fact that the Air Force price was a fluke. They hadn't purchased hydrogen in a long time so their price sheet was outdated, whereas NASA quoted the current cost. Our respective conclusions in hand, I smiled sheepishly at Mac not mentioning his "slight" error. No one, except my eagle-eyed boss, Jack Williams, noticed the maneuver. He wanted a propellant branch under his management and little ploy helped him pick who would run it…yours truly, of course.

* * *

Apollo 11 was on its way to the moon that day in July 1969. It was lunchtime and we were sitting around the table at the CCF and got into a conversation about the success of Apollo 10 and its flight around the moon and journey back to earth. Apollo 11 would be the historic moon landing. Dale, a mechanic, had been talking with one of the flight controllers over at the Launch Control Center about how critical the return to earth was.

"The final maneuver and aim to earth must be exact," Dale said, "And boy is it scary. The capsule is going backwards so that the heat shield is pointed to earth's atmosphere. In other words, the astronaut's can't see the earth. The flight angle must be within a very small margin. Too shallow and the capsule will skip off the atmosphere and head for the sun or outer space. Too deep of an angle and the capsule will burn up in the atmosphere as the heat shield can only provide a limited amount of protection. That's scary."

We talked of how many people would not know about this interesting fact.

* * *

It was the start of another sweltering August day in 1972 when I got a call from the KSC Duty Officer.

"Bain, one of your hydrogen trucks blew up last night just outside Tallahassee, Florida! We'll get more information for you soon, but it looks like a basket case."

Thirty minutes later, I got another call.

"Is this Mr. Bain?"

"Yes."

"I'm with the Florida Highway Patrol. There's a gage on the outside of that hydrogen truck that reads four-psig. What should we do?"

"Nothing!" I exclaimed. "Don't touch a thing. Just close the damn road and I'll be there with a team as soon as I can. Meet us at the Tallahassee airport."

"By the way I thought it was a basket case?"

The officer told me the fire department "put the fire out" and they had a wrecker company up right the tanker and that was when he noticed the pressure gage.

As we turned the corner onto Highway 90 near Tallahassee, we spotted the flashing blue lights. There it was, one of "my" 16,000-gallon liquid hydrogen tankers sitting upright, sadly darkened, but intact. George from propellants, and Tom from Safety, followed me over to the manifold plumbing at the rear of the tanker. The tanker manifold was so badly burned that we could not configure it to make a sniff (hydrogen) test. So, we unbolted the vent pipe and slid it around. George put the hydrogen detector probe up the pipe.

He looked up at me and declared, "It went off the scale!"

"Son-of-a-bitch!" I yelled. The problem was that we did not know how much air was in the inner tank, if any. So we assumed the worst condition since we could not test the contents of the inner tank directly.

The FHP had closed off only one lane. I turned to the officer and said, "There isn't time for me to explain the properties of hydrogen to you, so let me ask what you'd do if this were a truck loaded with unstable dynamite?"

Without a word, he dashed off and blocked the road at the nearest west intersection and the one towards the east. I called Gorman at the Cape and gave him a run down on the situation. I needed the OK to commit spending for supplies to inert the tanker. He told me to hang on as he called Bill Lohse on another line. Bill was head of KSC procurement. Bob told me to go ahead, Lohse "would keep me honest" when I got back! I used the officer's radio to dispatch available cylinders of inert gases, flex hoses, fittings, etc., from industrial gas suppliers and welding shops within a 50-mile radius of the site. That afternoon, we began purging the inner tank of the trailer. We were up all night. By 10 o'clock the next morning, we got a "safe" reading. As a backup, I ordered a tube bank of nitrogen from KSC the night before but I knew it wouldn't reach us till morning.

Shortly after sunrise, the crew from KSC arrived and found us sitting by the ditch. Neither of us paid heed to the fact that we were completely covered in black soot. George continuously apologized for the incident we had. It was during the night when incredibly, while in the midst of purging out the hydrogen, we accidentally knocked over a row of bottles. As they clanged together, sparks started flying! George panicked and knocked me over as he dove headfirst into the smoky ashes of the nearby brush.

I looked up and saw the KSC techs approaching.

One of them yelled, "Hey, you guys look like crap!"

To be on the safe side we hooked up their trailer and dumped the nitrogen into the hydrogen tanker. We got everything cleaned up and hauled off without any further mishaps.

As we were getting things together to head back to the Cape this guy approached me with a camera dangling around his neck. He presented me with his business card, which said he was a freelance photographer. He held out his hand and showed me two sets of film negatives. He claimed they were of the fire the night before. I said ok what's your deal. He responded, "500 bucks." Oh boy, a rip off, but I wanted to see the film. I checked with the highway patrolman and he indicated the guy really was there. So I made out a hand written promissory note. I thought to myself, I would work that out with NASA procurement later.

As it turned out one film was color the other in black and white. I had the NASA lab print me out 8 by 10 copies. I found the photos of great interest. Assembling other facts as best I could the event could be characterized. The tanker/truck obviously had jackknifed, turned over and slid on the pavement. The diesel fuel sidesaddle tank on one side of the truck ruptured and the fuel caught fire sending a fire front down the ditch toward the hydrogen tanker. The very thin outer shell of the hydrogen tanker was breached causing a loss in vacuum and thus the super cold hydrogen would vaporize. The excess pressure build up opened the tank relief valve and the hydrogen vented to the atmosphere. If you can picture this tanker lying on its side with the vent stack toward the brush on the roadside, the venting hydrogen catching fire and shooting a very large "blow torch" flame to ignite the brush. That was the scene. The color photos showed the typical bright red/orange/yellow carbon fire (brush, tires, tanker paint job, etc.). But, very interesting, the black and white photos showed the hydrogen fire plume out of the vent stack. The color photos were indicative that the hydrogen fire contribution was being masked by the radiant effect of the companion carbon based flame. Interesting. The hydrogen flame emission is mostly in the ultraviolet region (4340 angstroms and beyond) with some in the infrared region outside of our eyesight capabilities.

How much hydrogen? A little under two million cubic feet.

Fire

Tanker

Tom, George and me

* * *

We used a common carrier to haul the KSC hydrogen tankers. We experienced many problems and had to call in the FBI several times. They found that in one case drivers were trading the new tires on the KSC units with used tires at a truck stop. Two of the tankers were experiencing right rear fender damage. The FBI found that the drivers were stopping off the highway and visiting a whorehouse. Apparently it was difficult negotiating around an oak tree as they departed the house. We decided to transfer the tankers to the hydrogen supplier and let them be responsible for the units. The problems went away.

* * *

It was the fall of 1970 and I had found out that I was still entitled to the VA educational financial assistance program. I decided to enroll in the systems engineering masters' program.

The analytical methods, research methodology and behavioral science courses were quite a shift from the math, physics and chemistry of the Bachelor of Science program. But I was glad to complete the curriculum, as it later proved beneficial.

* * *

By 1973, my engineering responsibilities expanded to include all mobile propellants and gases equipment. I joined in with the team at each field operation to monitor how things were going and discovered that the technicians were not following the procedures step-by-step and were even skipping very simple "rules" of safety compliance. One day, during a hydrogen operation at Complex 39A, all hell broke loose.

The safety guy said, "Bain, go get your hard hat." I was there as only an observer that day. When actually operating the equipment I used my hard hat as it was a support for the safety face mask, which was another requirement.

"But, we aren't under any structure or overhead piping. The procedure doesn't specify it for this specific operation," I insisted.

"I don't care. Do as I say!" he hollered back.

"But, we don't do this in the Industrial Area and it's the same operation. I am keenly aware of the requirement when we support the fuel cell hydrogen operation at the service structure," I argued.

"I don't *care* what those safety guys do in the IA, *I'm* in charge here."

"Screw you!" I shouted, and stomped off in an unforgiving temper. That wasn't the only problem I was having with procedures that day. I was getting hard headed as my frustrations accumulated. Some problems appeared minor while others were serious and something needed to be done. I was perhaps fanatical in having accurate documentation.

Fifteen minutes later, I was called in to Bob Gorman's office with John Atkins. Bob was a stocky five-foot-five and liked to wear his light brown, thinning hair slicked straight back. Armed with a clear understanding of the politics of the space business, and well respected by his peers and co-workers, he was a man able to make sound decisions quickly. Atkins was the KSC Safety Director. Both of them reported to Debus.

"Bain, what the hell is going on with you?" Gorman demanded.

I immediately launched into a detailed description of my point of view on the status of procedures, the inconsistency with safety policies and the variables between sites, on policies and procedures.

"Moreover," I added, "a thorough shakedown is needed because the techs in the field have no respect for the written word!"

Gorman reached into his shirt pocket, pulled out his pack of Camels and lit one up. He puffed several times, slowly and deliberately, and his bright red face gradually faded back to its normal pasty white. Raising an eyebrow, he peered over his thin reading glasses at me and asked, "Do you have any specific examples?"

I had a copy of the "Hydrogen Procedure" and proceeded to circle, in red, the items in question. Atkins took interest in the safety guidelines section that had been copied from his organization's generalized guidebook. Then, simultaneously, Gorman and Adkins asked me what I thought the real problem was.

"I hate to say this," I said, "But, it looks like information is coming from a variety of organizational sections and over time, the changes made by the changing work force creates these inconsistencies and introduces' error without field validation. Also, equipment modifications are being made and the procedures are frequently not updated."

Atkins was still making his way through my red circles in "Hydrogen Procedure" while Gorman sat perfectly silent. After several minutes, he tapped his temple with his index finger and said, "I think I have an idea on how to solve some of this mess. Let me make a couple of phone calls and I'll get back with you this afternoon, okay?"

"You bet. I'll wait to hear from you," I said, and went back to my office.

About an hour later, Gorman called.

"Okay Addison, you were right about the problems, so here's what I plan to do. I've talked with the manager for Bendix, Dr. Al Bruckner, and we want you to coordinate with their head technical writer, a guy named Paul Christina, and set up a procedure validation program."

"Great, so when do I start?"

"Tomorrow morning. The Bendix group is located on the 42nd floor of the Vertical Assembly Building (VAB). Be there at eight."

The next morning, I made my way to the VAB building. There, I caught the elevator and rode the long ascent to the 42nd floor. The door to the Bendix office was wide open so I walked in and went straight to the blackboard at the other end of the room. I picked up a long piece of white chalk, inscribed the letters "B A I N" and proceeded to underline it with bold authority when the chalk made a loud "crack", snapped in half, and fell to the floor! I put down the remaining stub, wiped my hand on my trousers, and found a seat in front of Paul Christina's desk.

A minute later, this tall Italian-looking guy got up from behind his desk and also went to the blackboard. He took up a fresh piece of chalk, and with equal emphasis, he wrote "CHRISTINA." As he began to vigorously underline his name, his chalk also broke in half and we both burst out laughing. From that moment forward, Paul and I have been the best of friends. If you can visualize a tall guy with white hair neatly combed back, with hand made Italian shoes, in an Armani suit and think of Dapper Don, you got it.

Together, in 90 days, we cranked out 109 procedures, complete with field validation by the techs and the Quality Control and Safety Departments. The head of safety instituted a program to normalize their policy across all sites, and things finally began to run as expected. Not long thereafter, Gorman summoned me to his office to praise me for my efforts.

"By now you probably know, Addison, that we're redoing all procedures in other areas as well."

"Yeah, I know, and the rest of the guys are not sure if they should shake my hand or shoot me!" I laughed.

After work that Friday, we all decided to meet for Happy Hour at the Mouse Trap. As I approached the bar lounge, I spotted Jack Williams and John Atkins at a nearby table.

"How about a drink you guys?"

"Great idea," Atkins piped in.

Jack conceded and summoned the nearest mouse. A few drinks later, Atkins started talking about work and his concern over hydrogen procedures and policies.

"Bain, I've got a confession to make. You know, when you brought up that whole procedure issue, I must say, I thought you were too damn cavalier in the way you went about it!"

"What?" I responded. I felt ambushed.

Before I could come back at him, Jack stepped in. He leaned over into Atkins' face.

I heard him say, "John… Addison does not deal in the trivial. If anything, he's a maverick!"

Atkins just smiled and said nothing else.

* * *

After our new procedure program, I moved up through the ranks from engineering technician, to engineer, and ultimately to a management position. As Chief of the Propellants and Life Support Branch, and later, Chief of the Propellants Office, I oversaw the operations of acquisition, transport, and distribution of cryogenics, hypergolic propellants, compressed gases, fuels and specialty fluids in support of the NASA and Air Force programs at KSC and the Eastern Test Range.

* * *

Over the years I worked closely with the Air Force Logistics Command. One of their key people was Skip Carr. He managed to embarrass me one day on an issue with the supply of nitrogen to the Cape, so I called him an SOB in front of everyone. We were friends from then on. Together we solved a variety of propellant related issues. Tall, thin, slightly reddish hair, Skip was a ball to work with. He understood the politics very well. Through his effort we got the Air Force to agree to buy all their hydrogen using the NASA contracts. This was no easy task as the Air Force instituted hydrogen projects in the 50's and always contracted with private firms to build the necessary equipment and facilities to produce and deliver liquid hydrogen.

Never forgot the day I sketched out a diagram on a wet bar napkin suggesting a configuration for the Vandenberg nitrogen plant that needed to be built. Skip actually took it to his procurement office and insisted that was their technical input for the invitation for bid.

When at his office in San Antonio, we would leave early and tell everyone we were going to Procurement. When at my office at KSC we would say we were going to the Chem Lab. These were actually local bars. We worked hard, but played hard as well.

The last Apollo launch was #17. Skip and I learned from our management that the nitrogen plant just outside the gate was one of a number of facilities vulnerable to a possible terrorist attack. Within a few days the entire outskirts of the plant was made void of shrubbery and a security fence was installed, that's how well we worked together.

* * *

KSC formed a group to look at building a large plant that would produce, not only hydrogen, but also oxygen, nitrogen, heat and electricity. The concept was called "polygeneration."

On the NASA headquarters team there was a guy named Chic. Chic was a short, dynamic, and outspoken fellow with a Ph.D. tagged onto his name. He was another among us who loved to party. When he and I were on the road together, or at KSC after our team meetings, we would head for town after work.

"Add," he would say, "I get enough of those guys during the day. They're great to work with, but by the time cocktail hour rolls around, I can't stand to hear the word polygeneration."

Talking politics…well, that was a different story. Chic and

I hatched an idea to use the polygen project as a means to move hydrogen management from Huntsville to the Cape, followed by a transfer of headquarters activity for propellants. Jack Williams helped with the scheme, and it worked. The folks in Huntsville were left in a state of shock when we pulled it off.

At Jack's place, over scotches, we three formulated an organizational plan.

Jack said, "Add, you need to work quickly on this one."

Chic maneuvered the approval at headquarters using a write-up that we had prepared. At the same time, Jack revealed to me that a KSC shift was in the works and I would be going under Bob Long's organization. This was an opportunity for a promotion if things fell into place...*fast.*

The "single point management" concept for liquid hydrogen was created. The concept involved establishing an office at KSC that would oversee the management of liquid hydrogen for NASA as well as the Air Force. This led to the establishment of KSC contracts with industrial suppliers of liquid hydrogen. As a result, I set out on the road and visited hydrogen production plants and equipment suppliers, and attended a variety of national and international conferences and meetings. Chic was a good contact to have as he kept me aware of hydrogen activities going on at headquarters as well as some of the field centers. Of particular interest to me was the idea of using liquid hydrogen as an aircraft fuel—a concept under study by the Langley and Lewis centers.

* * *

In 1973, I had presented a hydrogen paper at a working conference at NASA's Langley Research Center in Virginia. The conference addressed the idea of fueling airplanes with hydrogen. It was there that I learned more of the story behind the Lockheed CL 400 proposal, and the SR 71 (Blackbird) idea to use hydrogen. The Air Force wanted a spy plane successor to the U-2 that would fly higher and faster. A supply of hydrogen fuel for engine testing was needed and West Palm, Florida, was designated as the site for building the first large-scale, liquid hydrogen plant. The locals were told that it was going to be a fertilizer plant.

Courtesy of Air Products & Chemicals, Inc.

West Palm LH2 Plant

Kelly Johnson, project leader of the famous supersecret Lockheed Skunk Works in Palmdale, California, decided he wanted the new airplane to be fueled with liquid hydrogen. The CIA had indications that the Russians were on a crash program to develop a hydrogen powered airplane at the time. But, after many adjustments to the design, the CL 400 would not have the range it needed. It would require strategically placed hydrogen tank farms in Europe and Asia to accommodate refueling. The US was having enough problems with supplying the special jet fuel to the U-2 refueling base in

Turkey. So, the CL 400 project was cancelled. The Air Force continued to develop the Blackbird but opted to use jet fuel instead.

* * *

Bill Escher and Dick Foster of E:F Technology did a great job developing a study, per my arrangement, on a project plan for implementing a hydrogen-fueled, hydrogen transport rail system. I called it the LH2 unit train. I was already in the process of having the only NASA-owned liquid hydrogen railcars shipped to KSC from Lewis Research Center in Cleveland. I planned to use the railcars to transport liquid hydrogen from the production plant in New Orleans to the Cape. The boil-off hydrogen would be used to fuel the locomotive, thus operating a total hydrogen train. Using a unit train concept would reduce the travel time and the transport cost. The four cars on liquid hydrogen were just enough to support a Space Shuttle launch abort turnaround, another plus with the idea.

The railcars were put into service for a while, but I was unable to score any funding to go the next step and modify one of NASA's locomotives. Using the customary rail system, the turnaround and cost was not achievable due to the switching required between rail companies along the route.

"We are in the launch business, not a research center," I was told.

To this day, I still get aggravated when I drive by and see those railcars still sitting on their rail spur, slowly and silently rusting away. I have an HO gauge model of the hydrogen unit train in my office along with an "O" gauge model of the LH2 modified locomotive. I still have all the drawings and specs to do the job. Oh well.

Dr. Nejat Veziroglu, a professor of Turkish origin, organized a meeting that was attended by a couple of dozen engineers, scientists and professors with hydrogen backgrounds. We came from all over the world for this initial rendezvous in a Miami hotel. Together, we founded the International Association for Hydrogen Energy and laid plans for our first conference. We decided to call it "THEME" and scheduled it for March 1974, once again in Miami. Every two years, since then, the conferences have taken place in a different international location, which has afforded me the opportunity to travel to such places as Moscow, Paris, Stuttgart and Buenos Aires. In 2002, Association attendance reached over 800.

At one of our 1980 meetings, a few of us gathered in the hotel suite of Dr. Edward Teller and his wife, Mici. Teller, characterized by his large, bushy eyebrows and his slow, methodical speech was labeled "the Father of the Hydrogen Bomb" after the Second World War. Our conversation that evening was fascinating! We discussed the unfortunate negative public perception of nuclear power plants due to the "Three Mile Island" nuclear plant incident that had occurred the year before. The stigma of it had virtually closed the public's mind to most non-traditional sources of energy generation. We agreed, that if not for that, an ideal source of energy could be put into place for producing hydrogen.

* * *

In 1989, myself and a group of 4 Americans, 4 Russians, 2 Frenchmen, 1 Japanese and 3 Germans, all professionals working with hydrogen, met in Zurich to form what would later be known as the International Standards Organization (ISO) Hydrogen Technologies TC 197. This was the beginning of an international attempt to develop standards for hydrogen.

That same year, we had a meeting at EPRI, the Electric Power Research Institute in Palo Alto, California, and the foundation for the National Hydrogen Association (NHA) was laid. This was a movement within the United States to form a professional society to address hydrogen issues. With the help of a representative from Airco, we formulated the first NHA document, a brochure on hydrogen safety.

I continued to participate in many hydrogen conferences and meetings on a regular basis, but found the majority of the presentations of the day were long, drawn out, theoretical dissertations. Some time later, I began to notice reports about people like Frank Lynch, Roger Billings, and Ben Jordan who were starting to use hydrogen in practical daily applications that protected the environment at the same time. One such use was the conversion of cars, retrofitting them to use hydrogen as a fuel. Their writings stepped out of the ordinary and inspired me with some ideas of my own.

* * *

Toward the end of 1982, I approached Dave Block and Kirk Collier at the local solar center, and proposed a NASA applications project. We discussed the idea of building a concentrating solar collector, a single photovoltaic cell connected to an electrolyzer, to produce hydrogen to store in containers. The project was completed and tested at the solar center, but it was not installed at KSC as planned. I needed facility funding, which was not approved. Once again, I was reminded, "KSC was not a research facility!" We went on ten years later with a project to fuel a Ford Crown Vic with a mixture of natural gas and hydrogen. Most of the work was completed before the investigators went on to another job. Years later I became the owner of the same Ford.

* * *

Speaking of colleague Ben Jordan, he learned of my interest in hydrogen many years ago through contacts he had made with hydrogen investigators under contract with the Department of Energy doing a variety of research projects in their labs. Ben built a hydrogen-fueled internal combustion engine in 1932, a couple of years before he attended Clemson University. He has since committed himself to the promotion of "Hydrogen as the vehicle fuel of our future." He has challenged the encyclopedia and automotive historians stating that the first automobile was the one built by German engineer Karl Benz, in 1885. His extensive research into the subject reveals that it was Isaac de Rivaz who built the first "engine-powered wagon," in 1805. The vehicle had four wheels, weighed over 2,000 pounds, and was seventeen feet long, and ran on hydrogen and other gaseous mixtures. Whereas the Benz was not really a "car" at all but a flimsy tricycle with a three-quarter horsepower single cylinder engine. It was not until 1893 that Benz built his first four-wheeled vehicle, the Victoria.

Ben and I have shared much information about hydrogen. He and his wife, Barbara, offer a trophy every year at the Bonneville Salt Flats land speed record event, for any vehicle running on hydrogen. He converted and drove the first hydrogen-fueled piston-engine vehicle ever to run at the Bonneville Salt Flats in Utah on September 21, 1981 at about 120 mph. Ben has also built a model airplane engine that runs on hydrogen. In view of my interests in building models he has given it to me. The objective is for us to have the first model airplane in the air running on hydrogen. One big hurdle is the Academy of Model Aeronautics "approving" the use of hydrogen at any sanctioned event. So far "hydrogen" is too dangerous, so they say, while the poisonous, highly flammable nitromethane fuels used in models is approved. Unbelievable!

* * *

I met Doctor G, as I call him, at a social gathering in Cocoa Beach. He had a local medical practice and was also doing work with the University of Florida where they were experimenting with a drink for athletes. The drink would be used to compensate for the loss of not only water, but electrolytes and other ingredients for the active athlete, as well as provide an energy boost. He told me about the first batch they made.

"Addison, it tasted like urine, so they had to come up with more additives."

But then he got the notion to be a politician, and was elected to a seat in the Tallahassee legislature. We had gotten on the subject of hydrogen and he became interested in how it could be used as auto fuel. I explained the history and progress so far with the work by a number of researchers and loaded him up with papers and articles on the subject. So he came up with a plan to enter legislation at the capitol in Tallahassee spelling out a $100,000 prize for the first car to win a race at the Daytona racetrack running on hydrogen. I had gotten a tentative arrangement for a hydrogen supplier to provide the fuel at the track for them to gain a little PR with the project, and perhaps ease the minds of track officials by having hydrogen experts on hand. Then the news hit the local paper that he and his wife were killed in a small plane on the way back from Tallahassee. I did not pursue the project any further. It was tough enough to sell hydrogen at the state capitol. By the way, the drink was finally named ...Gatorade.

* * *

In the fall of 1984, the polygeneration team set out to visit energy and hydrogen production plants in the US. We used a NASA plane, a turbo prop Gulfstream, and flew to West Virginia to visit a coal plant, and then on to the Solar One facility in Barstow, California. We stopped in Santa Maria, California to refuel and rest for the night. The next day, en route back to Florida, we were at cruising altitude when the engines stopped! Dick, our team leader, was up front talking with the pilot. Suddenly, he rushed from the cockpit, face as white as a sheet, took his seat and firmly buckled himself in.

"We're going down!" he hollered.

It's a strange sound when a powered aircraft suddenly becomes a glider. Stranger still is when that swooshing, gliding sound has drowned out the pounding of your own panicking heart!

I had a flash back to the time in high school when we took out a Cessna 172 and played roller coaster with the Continental Divide. We flew the 172 under the Old Steel Bridge to buzz my classmates, having a graduation party. That was supposed to be fun, but now things were not so fun.

Our pilot called ahead to Albuquerque and requested permission for an emergency landing. In the meantime, he set his flight plan to keep within the air space of Interstate 40 since the landing strip was still a good distance away. He suspected that the fuel we had picked up in Santa Maria might have contained water that turned to ice when we gained altitude. In addition to that, the heaters on the fuel filters failed, causing a blockage in the fuel line. He decided to lower our altitude and by doing so it allowed the plane's fuel system to slowly warm up. Finally, the pilot was able to restart one of the engines. Our aircraft, the NASA 4, limped along in the sky right up until our landing at Patrick Air Force Base, Florida. At the beginning of the trip, we had several teetotalers in the group. But, by the time the tires kissed the tarmac, I can assure you, there wasn't a drop of liquor left on board!

* * *

It was in 1985 when NASA Administrator, Jim Beggs, appointed me to go to Vandenberg Air Force Base in California to assist with propellants, life support, precision cleaning, laboratory sampling and analysis functions in support of the Space Shuttle Program. Beggs had presented me with the Exceptional Service Medal just before I left for California. I always thought he had a great vision for NASA's future.

Then, with the Challenger accident in January 1986, there was a decommissioning of the facilities at the base and I returned to Kennedy Space Center in Florida to serve as a technical assistant in ground operations.

One day, I received a brochure in the mail from the International Association for Hydrogen Energy (IAHE). A conference had been scheduled to take place in Moscow, in September 1988. I wanted to attend, so I approached my new boss, Jim Rice, to ask for approval. He was required to go to the "fourth floor" to get the okay. His request was refused on the grounds that someone from our design engineering organization would be more qualified to go. But Jim knew that I had more contact with the hydrogen community than anyone else. So, he took it upon himself to ignore the opinion and went directly to NASA's Washington, DC Headquarters and obtained authorization for me to attend.

Without advance notice, I was summoned by NASA Security, the FBI, and the CIA to attend some confidential briefings. At first, I was stunned by their insistence that we discuss my impending journey, but I soon understood their motivation. They wanted to instruct me on how to search for spying devices that might possibly be concealed in my Moscow hotel room. And, they cautioned me not to meet secretly with anyone during my stay in Russia. All of a sudden, I felt like I'd just stepped into a James Bond movie!

After boarding the Aeroflot jet at JFK Airport, I settled in for a trip that was going to be much longer than anything I was used to. I was never one to engage in conversation on flights. I preferred to sleep which seemed to make the time pass quickly.

As our plane approached the terminal, I spotted military personnel canvassing the area armed with machine guns. Disembarkment seemed to take forever and was followed by a long wait in the terminal for the ride to my hotel. Finally, an English speaking man appeared and said "Mr. Bain, your ride is ready." He pointed to a nearby bus. I looked in all directions but saw no one else approaching. I concluded that I was to be the one and only passenger, so I boarded and sat in the seat nearest the driver. The other 39 seats remained empty. It took about forty minutes to arrive in Moscow.

Upon check-in, the hotel clerk confiscated my passport. This made me feel extremely uneasy, so the next day, I phoned the American Embassy. A kind, young-sounding man came on the line and said, "Yes, Mr. Bain, we know you're here. The KGB and the local police are reviewing your situation and should release your passport soon."

"*Thanks a lot, Ruskies,*" I thought as I hung up the phone. I was already nervous enough walking the streets of Moscow, and now with no passport, I was doubly anxious. The Cold War was still ongoing and the thought of getting stuck in Russia terrified me.

On my third day there, I presented my paper before the USSR Academy of Sciences. It was entitled "Liquid Hydrogen: Production and Utilization in the USA - Past, Present and Future." My speech was well received and I was pleased with the applause from the audience as I stepped down from the podium. I made my way to the rear of the conference room that easily accommodated the 600 attendees.

Suddenly, as if from out of nowhere, I saw three men approaching. The one in the middle was dressed in civilian clothes and two, square jawed military men in black uniforms closely flanked him. The soldier on his left said something in Russian, then stepped forward and pointed directly at me. I froze in my tracks, not knowing what to expect. I was soon relieved to learn that the civilian was Peter Vassilyev of Radio Moscow World Services, and he had come to ask me for an interview.

We made our way to an isolated table in the corner and pulled up some chairs while he set up his tape recorder. The discussion began with questions about hydrogen and the space program. Then, in a remarkably sly manner, my interviewer began to approach the subject of American military missile capabilities.

Whoa, I thought, *this stuff is being taped.*

Visions of briefings I'd attended on the secret Air Force Titan and Atlas / Agena projects loomed in my mind. I had routinely attended the secret briefings to address propellant requirements for the launch vehicle and payloads. So at that point, I shut down the interview. Somewhat later at the conference, members of the USSR State Committee for

Standards approached me, followed by other "hydrogen" people, but I remained on high alert.

By the last day of the conference, all of this intrigue had become nerve-wracking, so I decided to look for a place to have a drink. I remembered a little hole-in-the-wall pub I'd spotted near my hotel the day before.

I was glad to come in out of the chilly night air and hurriedly pulled up a stool at the bar. I was unfamiliar with the local cocktails, and not a big fan of vodka, so I ordered a Russian beer. I couldn't read the writing on the label, but it didn't taste half bad, kind of a cross between a western dark and a Coors.

Halfway through my brew, I was overwhelmed by a sweet-smelling perfume. A moment later, an attractive woman, who looked like she'd just stepped out of a Cosmopolitan magazine page, sat down on the barstool next to me and ordered a drink. Her long, platinum blonde hair was fashionably styled. She had striking Russian features with a fair complexion. Tall and slim, her figure looked like it had been poured into the body suit she was wearing. I thought, at the time, that her purse was just big enough for a pack of cigarettes, or perhaps a miniature tape recorder, recalling my instructions to be cautious.

"You are an American," she stated, in perfect English. "My name is Elke. What is yours?"

"Uhm…Addison," I replied hesitantly.

"What an interesting name. What do you do?" she asked. She kept her eyes intently fixed on my face as she waited for my response.

"I'm an engineer at NASA," I replied. Coincidentally, we had just seen the launch of a Shuttle on the small television behind the bar.

"Well, that is fascinating. Why are you in Moscow?" she asked as she casually opened her purse, pulled out a pack of cigarettes, and set it on the bar between us.

I told her about the conference and we soon began discussing the subject of hydrogen. She led the way with a barrage of precise questions: how is hydrogen used for rockets, what plans did NASA have for future missions, what do the satellites do, are they used for surveillance, and how many are there? She continued with, "I recently read somewhere that satellites in space can actually read the license plate of a car on earth."

I looked at her, continued sipping my beer, and said nothing.

"Is NASA planning to go back to moon? And, what about Mars?" she inquired. She tilted her head flirtatiously and waited for my reply. I still said nothing but she forged ahead with, "do they build rockets for the military?"

It was clear that *this lady* had been briefed. She knew who I was and she knew her subject well. I smiled politely, turned to the barman, and motioned for another beer. At that point, my little Russian Mata Hari began to squirm on her chair, picked up the pack of cigarettes and returned it to her purse. Then, she skillfully changed the subject.

"Are you going to buy things here to take back to America?"

"Yes, I'll probably look around for some souvenirs for my wife and mother. I just exchanged some dollars for rubles."

"There is a big department store in the center of town called Gums. You should be able to find some things there. You know, you seem like a nice man, so while we are on the subject, are you interested in exchanging some more money? I could get you a good deal for your US dollars, about ten to one with the ruble. We could go to my apartment to make the transaction," she whispered softly.

"Thanks, but no thanks," I replied in an even tone of voice, hoping not to show even the slightest speck of interest.

"Well then, good luck with your shopping, and have a nice stay in Moscow," she said.

With that, she slid off her barstool, picked up her purse, and made her way to the door. My eyes couldn't help but follow her shapely figure to the exit. Suddenly, she turned and smiled back at me.

"Goodbye, Mr. Bain," she said. Then, she winked and closed the door behind her.

I breathed a long sigh and thought, "Wow, so much for unwinding, Russian-style!"

Then, bingo… it hit me. I hadn't told her my last name nor did she ever light up a cigarette! Funny thing about that!

The following morning, at the aerospace museum outside of Moscow, I was amazed that I was allowed to take pictures of Russian rocket engines. The first thing that I noticed was the poor welding of the fuel line piping joints. It looked like some of my work with my little Lincoln arc welder back in Huntsville. It was obvious that the engines were literally hand built. On the far side of the museum, I could see a mock-up of the Apollo / Soyuz configuration, but for some reason, it was strictly off limits.

Following that, I took a tour of Red Square. I found the interior of the Kremlin fascinating. I paused and tried to imagine Lenin or Stalin peering down from a balcony, surveying their military might as it paraded by, as I'd often seen in television documentaries.

Evidence of Russia sliding toward serious economic crisis

was everywhere. As I wandered the streets, I saw poverty, limited food supplies, and a greatly devalued monetary situation. I bought my wife a leather purse for about five dollars, clearly a tenth of its true value. For Mom, I purchased an exquisitely carved wooden plate that depicted the details of the Moscow skyline. Each time I traveled, I tried to return home with a plate for her extensive collection that literally wallpapered her kitchen in Kalispell.

I must confess that I felt a deep sense of relief when I finally boarded the plane to New York. Even the layover in Frankfort was a reprieve. Once back in the US, however, I was again besieged with interrogations by US authorities concerning my trip. NASA Security was the first to call, followed by a debriefing, then a get-together with the FBI at a local restaurant.

Soon after, while on a trip to Washington, DC, the CIA called on me in my Marriott room in Crystal City. In a later meeting, they took me to a room suspended within a vault in a nearby federal building where I was asked to present a briefing on hydrogen production technologies. They showed me a satellite image of what appeared to be a hydrogen plant under construction in a foreign country. It was obvious to me that it was in close proximity to a space vehicle launch site. It was easy to identify the process and plant size. Two cars that appeared in the image were a good reference of measurement. I described, to the eight men and one woman who were present, that one could determine possible launch vehicle parameters based on sizing of the propellant tanks on the launch pad. They all stared at me with blank expressions and said nothing. Their silence was eerie. I would have preferred if they'd at least asked me a few questions. Instead, I came away with no clue of what they were thinking.

I continued my correspondence with members of the USSR State Committee for Standards with hydrogen as the key topic. Subsequently, I was invited to attend a special gathering of Internationals to discuss hydrogen. The meeting was to be held on a boat trip on a waterway flowing out from Kazan, Russia. When I received the invitation list, I saw that it was mainly comprised of Russian and Chinese nationals, and two Iraqis. Plans were set in motion for me to attend. Funds to be provided by the US State Department, but NASA would appear as the authorizing agency. I had my blue passport, but was instructed to use the red one previously issued to me by the State Department. Once again, I was summoned for a pre-trip briefing. Only this time, much to my alarm, I was informed that if something happened to me, the US would "have to disavow any knowledge of my trip, my whereabouts or my state of being."

I concluded all bets were off!

I did, however, continue to correspond with individuals at Leningrad State University, St. Petersburg State University, and the USSR Academy of Sciences. The occasional meetings and coded STU III telephone conversations with US intelligence departments continued until it was evident that the Russian economy was collapsing.

A few years later, I learned that our government was grooming me as a double agent, that is, the Russians would have been convinced I was working with them, while I would actually be working for US intelligence. The common denominator of course was hydrogen, which "allowed" me to find out about space and military operations in Russia. I did find out how they transferred liquid hydrogen from transporters to the main storage tanks at the launch pads. They filled the pad storage tanks using remote controls, quite different than at KSC. They showed me photos of the operation. Looking back on it now really gives me the willies. This naive Montana boy had no idea what they'd had in mind for me.

* * *

The future of hydrogen as a significant fuel especially in the liquid form to support the aviation industry concerns me in terms of the close relationship with helium. Helium will not freeze at liquid hydrogen temperatures, is inert, and therefore makes it a good purging agent for hydrogen systems. That is, helium will be an important element needed for hydrogen systems. It is rare and expensive. The industry has come up with ideas to minimize the use of helium such as the vacuum purge technique. However I wish to document some background about it.

The source of helium on earth is the slow process of radioactive decay of certain elements. A byproduct of billions of years of decay, helium is distilled from natural gas that has accumulated in the presence of radioactive uranium and thorium deposits.

Prior to the 1920's helium was found in very small quantities in natural gas. Recoverable concentrations were primarily found in the Texas, Oklahoma, and Kansas area known as the Hugoton Field. This led to the enactment of The Helium Act of 1925, assigning the management responsibility to the Secretary of the Interior. The finding that in the entire world only the US may have helium resources led to national security concerns.

Prior to WW II, the US government programs represented most of the helium demand. Operations were assigned to the Bureau of Mines. In spite of the development of medical, scientific and commercial uses of helium in the 1950's the private sector production did not develop until after the 1960 Helium Act Amendment.

An important provision of the Act was that the private sector was encouraged to develop a helium supply. Another provision was the creation of a conservation program to save helium from being wasted to the atmosphere with the consumption of helium-bearing natural gas. Helium was extracted from natural gas by a cryogenic process and stored in the underground field known as the Cliffside gas field. It was then drawn off as needed, purified and made available for market. Although some helium has been found in other countries, the US still produces 90% of the worldwide demand.

In the 1970's it appeared that the forecasts for helium were optimistic and then more helium rich natural gas was discovered in the Riley Ridge field in Wyoming. The conservation program was also heavy in debt. These factors led to the cancellation of the conservation program. The private sector production and distribution of helium was also accelerating. Then a decision was made in 1989 for the Bureau of Mines to phase out and turn over operations to the private sector.

A letter to the speaker of the house from the Secretary of Interior on May 22, 1989, states; "We believe that the private sector, given proper assurances that the Federal Government will not compete in the market place under normal conditions, can and will be able to adequately supply helium to the Federal and private customers. Therefore, the Federal helium program, as originally structured, is no longer necessary."

The cancellation of the conservation program caused uproar in the scientific community. The American Physical Society issued the following warning; "In view of the importance of this unique and irreplaceable natural resource to modern science and technology, the APS urges that measures be adopted that will both conserve and enhance the nation's helium reserves. Failure to do so would not only be wasteful, but would be economically and technologically shortsighted."

Over the years during my NASA career I maintained close contact with the Bureau of Mines, especially during the time I managed the helium operations at KSC and the Cape. I visited the main office in Amarillo a number of times. The Bureau took me on tours of the plants, like at Exell and Keyes. My last visit was to the liquid helium plant at Exell. At the Amarillo plant were the facilities to test and maintain the railcars used to ship the helium.

When discussing the future availability of helium, one official at the Bureau said,

"Addison we have enough helium stored underground to last for 90 years."

As I write this, the thought occurs to me that was 35 years ago.

Helium is interesting stuff. Helium has a variety of isotopes (different forms). Natural helium is a mix of two stable isotopes, helium 3 and helium 4. In helium obtained from natural gas, about one atom in 10 million is helium 3. The unstable isotopes helium 5, 6 and 8 have been created synthetically. Helium 4 is unusual in that it can form two kinds of liquids when it is cooled below its boiling point. Ever hear about absolute zero? That is where all molecular motion stops and the lowest temperature you can get. Well just about 4 degrees (Kelvin) above absolute zero helium condenses to what is called helium I and behaves as an ordinary liquid. But taking it down to about 2 degrees liquid helium II is formed. It is sometimes called a superfluid because it has extremely low viscosity. It cannot be contained in an open beaker since the thin film of it creeps up the side, over the top, and flows down the outside. Defying gravity!

Helium 3 is also very interesting. It actually is a fuel. When reacted with deuterium considerable energy is released. It does not produce radioactive by-products like the nuclear fission reactors of today. There is little helium 3 on earth, but lots of it on the moon. Over many eons helium 3 has been deposited on the moon from the solar wind. One scientist estimates over a million tons of it at the surface, concentrated in the lunar Maria. To put this in perspective, about 25 tons of helium 3 would power the United States for a year. That amount would fill a railroad boxcar or a Space Shuttle payload bay. Some one has worked out that this helium is worth about three billion dollars a metric ton. Now that works out to be about $80,000 per ounce, talk about gold, no wonder China wants to beat us (back) to the moon.

* * *

At the end of 1991, I returned from a one-year stint at NASA Headquarters. I was given the assignment to look into implementing natural gas at KSC. I immediately got with the local gas company. That is when I met up with Randy Harris. His father actually started the business years before. Randy was new at the business, we hit it off at first acquaintance. We learned that a natural gas pipeline was proposed for KSC when NASA was constructing the KSC facilities back in the 1960's. The company, City Gas, offered to run a pipeline to the boundary line at KSC if NASA would carry it through the space center. At the time only the boilers at the KSC industrial area and Complex 39 utility annex would have been possible candidates for natural gas fuel. NASA decided to go to cheap, dirty, fuel oil.

Over a period of two years, Randy and I worked on all the technical, political, and related issues, laying the groundwork to counter the suspected reasons for not putting in a pipeline. I had heard that many attempts were made to start a project. I found that NASA had proposed a Construction of Facilities project, but it was way down on the priority list. I also learned that KSC "management" said NASA Headquarters would never go for it. All this information did was stir me up. I felt challenged. Reading through the federal regulations I found that government entities had to get an OK from the General Services Administration (GSA). Knowing this would be either a roadblock or another excuse to not put in the pipeline, I went to Washington DC to GSA Headquarters and located the individual that could help with giving KSC a delegation of authority so NASA could proceed on their own. This was only one of the many obstacles to overcome.

Then one day Randy called, "Add, lets meet at the Pineda Inn for a drink. I have been working the issues pertinent to my side of the fence and I need to get up to speed where you are on your side." Together we were prepared to address the issues. I told Randy I had scheduled a briefing for the KSC Director and his staff the following week. The briefing went, to my surprise, very smoothly. A lot of good questions, but I was ready for them and had the answers. Direction was given to proceed.

On September 23, 1993, my 58th birthday, KSC Center Director, ex-astronaut, Bob "Crip" Crippen, signed the contract for National Utility Investors/City Gas to build the pipeline to serve over 20 facilities. Another aspect of the project was for a very unique compressed natural gas (CNG) fueling station to fuel CNG vehicles. Now that was a mind blower! My wife, Sharon, attended the contract signing ceremony. Sharon thought Crip was very charming. He came over and shook her hand. She didn't wash her hands for a long time after that! Except for the NASA folks, we all went out to celebrate.

The pipeline was designed to provide enough gas capacity to support future energy projects as well as serving the feedstock requirements of an on-site liquid hydrogen plant to support future space missions and perhaps other hydrogen projects. This was something Randy and I kept to our chest until the project was completed. I was happiest about that!

"You know Randy, this kills coal-fired polygen," I laughed, as we downed a couple of vodka tonics at the Pineda Inn.

* * *

It was once again time for the Twins in Montana. This time Dad had a small camper trailer so we did not have to sleep on the ground. Seems like the fishing gets slower all the time as more people learn of the area. The selection of dry flies gets more challenging. Dad said he had a new problem for me to work on. He had been observing the wildfires in the forests since the big one he had to help fight in 1929, and he had come to a conclusion.

"You know, the air we breathe is exactly 21% oxygen. How in the hell can it stay that way if trees make oxygen and oxygen is also burned up from the air during the fire? How can nature assure us of a constant and proper amount?"

"Wow, I don't know Dad," I said.

"Well you better pick out a tree and preserve it," he laughed.

I sent Dad a recent book on the universe that Christmas. It gave the latest information on the cosmos. Along with it I included a bookmark I had made. It included my picture and the following inscription, "As you use this bookmark to keep tab on those moments to read about our magnificent universe, please reflect on your loving son, who likewise observes the marvels of matter, energy and life in the exciting prospect to try and understand the elusive creator of it all."

* * *

Since my retirement from NASA in 1994, I have continued to concentrate on hydrogen related activities. As one of the first members of the Department of Energy's Hydrogen Technical Advisory Panel, I served for six years and contributed to the NHA codes and standards activities. As the convener of the International Standards Organization WG3, I oversaw the development and publication of the first ISO TC 197 Standard, "Hydrogen Fuel - Product Specification." This provided for an international standard for hydrogen fuel in all applications from residential and commercial use to cars, buses, trains, planes and rockets.

On occasion, I glimpse reminders of my professional career. One example was an evening when I rented the newly released video "Apollo 13" starring Tom Hanks. A scene appeared in the film where Hanks was standing near the Space Shuttle crawler-transporter. I then noticed in the background the high-pressure piping.

I freeze-framed the tape so I could get a good look at it. There, in the background, as big as life, were the above ground high-pressure helium and nitrogen pipelines that I had designed nearly 40 years ago! Not bad since their predicted life was about 20 years.

When all is said and done, and I look back over my career, I have to admit that my most exciting and gratifying project of all simply started with three little words…"its hydrogen exploded!"

Those words, engraved on a plaque in the Smithsonian Air and Space Museum, launched me on a long adventure. From that moment forward, I knew I wouldn't be satisfied until I uncovered the truth about the *Hindenburg*.

Chapter 4

The Plaque

I was at my desk in a new assignment with NASA at NASA Headquarters in Washington DC. It was a one year Professional Development Program (PDP). The PDP provided the opportunity to become acquainted with all of the major offices at headquarters and participate in many classes held "on the Hill." The classes provided an education in the variety of activities that go on at our nation's capital. These included how bills, budgets, and projects are formulated, processed, approved and implemented. We (the PDP participants) were able to visit the offices of many congressional members and attend their hearings.

Ed Gabris was my mentor for the PDP program. He introduced me to many people engaged in advanced space projects, from technical people to budget and administration folks. He was of small to medium build and would move about the hallways such that I would almost have to run to keep up with him. He certainly was well seasoned in the politics "of the game." At times his slight smile revealed to me how he had this uncanny ability to read people. He taught me how to do what is termed "viewgraph engineering." This was a quick way of outlining a proposed project, giving it status and promoting it. I kept wanting to get into detail and make sure all the "i's" were dotted and "t's" crossed. He finally weaned me into staying focused on the big picture. He made sure I was dealing with the right people at the right time. I learned a lot.

I was working in the Advanced Program Office. Future concepts in launch rockets were being studied in that office. Down the hall some people were working on concepts for a Mars mission and in another office, far-out propulsion ideas were under study such as ion propulsion using high temperature hydrogen called a plasma. I was familiar with the gas, liquid, solid and slush states of hydrogen but this one was new to me.

Ron, the Director of the Advanced Program Office, was aware of my interest and background with hydrogen. Ron was aware of my hydrogen contacts in the industry and at the various government agencies and universities.

He called me in one day and said, "Add how about putting together a symposium on hydrogen leak detection. The issue has a lot of interest within the agency and apparently in the Department of Energy on what the state of the art is and where more research was needed."

He went on to say, in his usual methodical mannerism, "NASA has some program money to put toward detection projects."

I was aware that the last real effort to update the technology status on methods of hydrogen detection was a NASA survey done back in 1970, some 21 years prior.

Johnson Space Center, in Houston, played host to the event. The turn out was better than I expected with most of the agency centers being represented along with industry and academia making their presentations. Astronaut John

Young attended as he had a keen interest in advancing the technology.

My time in Washington wasn't always work. Our nation's capitol is full of all kinds of museums, monuments, interesting architecture and parks. My wife and I toured them whenever we got the chance.

One day I was looking out the third floor window of the old NASA Headquarters building on 600 Independence, over to the Smithsonian National Air & Space Museum across the street. I had visited it on a few occasions while on business trips to Washington, DC. I liked to wander around and look at the airplanes on display, but of special interest were the rockets. The small rockets pioneered by professor Robert Goddard and the German V-2 rocket designed by von Braun were my favorites.

The displays from the Apollo Program era made me sad to think the US stopped going to the moon and had not pursued the planned Mars mission using the proposed giant NOVA rocket. I remember when von Braun was disturbed over the fact President Nixon was talked into selecting the Space Shuttle configuration with the solid rocket boosters. Von Braun wanted a total cryogenic propelled vehicle, using liquid hydrogen and oxygen, with a fly back booster—a booster that flies back to the launch area once the Orbiter is well on it's way to orbit—no solid rocket boosters of any kind. Congress did not go for the higher, up-front costs of that option, even though the launch costs would have been considerably less. In retrospect I suspect there are many retired NASA folks and some ex-congressmen thinking the advice of the great rocket pioneer should have been heeded. Von Braun certainly rolled over in his grave when the Challenger accident happened.

Occasionally I had lunch at the Smithsonian cafeteria and then wandered about the rest of the museum. One day I noticed a large model of the *Hindenburg* hanging from the ceiling near the gift shop. It was about 28 feet long and had been used by Universal Studios for a movie with George C. Scott and Anne Bancroft. The story was based on the sabotage theory, inconsistent with the Board of Inquiry investigation conclusion, but nevertheless it provided the basis for an exciting story.

On the wall next to the model was a plaque (Smithsonians' call them labels). It briefly described the airship design and that fatal day at Lakehurst, New Jersey. But what got my attention were the words, "Its hydrogen exploded." Bullshit! I thought. Yeah the hydrogen would burn, but sixteen gas cells are not going to blow up without some air in them. In fact, they needed 40 percent air at best.

It didn't take much mental gymnastics to conclude the airship couldn't fly with that much air contamination.

My investigation into the *Hindenburg* disaster was launched at that moment!

Since I knew the pure hydrogen could not explode, I knew there had to be more to the story. I had to find out what information the Smithsonian had. I met with officials at the museum and they assigned a young man to work with me. It was required that I have someone with me at all times as I went through their files. The young, small, slim man named Alex obviously knew where to take me into all the records they had on airships and the *Hindenburg* disaster. He seemed very knowledgeable about the *Hindenburg*.

Alex asked, " Mr. Bain what prompted you to be looking into the subject?"

"Well," I said, "I have a problem with that dumb statement

on the plaque downstairs, the part about the hydrogen exploded."

He replied, "I have to tell you I came up with the wording for the label."

We actually worked quite well together after that.

First was scheduling access to the rare book room to read the original transcript of the Board of Inquiry. That was when I found out about the numerous file folders containing related information, newspaper articles and such. On most occasions the young man worked with me and at other times he would have someone else accompany me. I donned the white gloves and took notes with pencil. Ink pens were prohibited. The people at the Smithsonian were very helpful, leading me to other archives in the Washington, DC, area and making arrangements for me to meet the right people who would give me access to what I needed.

The research caused me to visit the various archives

National Archives

numerous times and I progressively managed to read all there was on the *Hindenburg* as well as some of the other airships. NASA had a library of airship material as well, transferred from its predecessor NACA, the National Advisory Committee for Aeronautics.

I was really interested in accumulating the number of photos of the disaster from a variety of sources. I thought by putting them together in some logical sequence, a pattern of the event could be developed. To my surprise, over time I acquired photos from individuals that were not in the archives and apparently were never published. Coupling this with the testimony of the observers I thought a story could be developed and any of the minor conflicts resolved.

Why, for example in one photo frame were two tanks dropping?

There was no discussion of this in the testimony. Discussion with some airship people indicated the action of releasing the tanks was to drop ballast, an action to lighten the airship. The problem with that explanation was, there were no crewmembers at that location to do it. Dropping ballast would have not been automatic and furthermore, it would have caused the bow of the airship to rise, not a good idea. Clearly the pattern of the activity in the photos was not matching the Board's conclusion, further increasing my curiosity.

Certain aspects of the investigation were not addressed, unlike the scrutiny of modern airplane disaster investigations today. For example, why was there little discussion about the make-up of the outer cover of the airship? Some preliminary reading of a variety of books on airships indicated that powdered aluminum/iron oxide mixed in with a cellulose nitrate paint (dopant) was used to coat the cover of many airships. The coating protected it and provided reflection of the sun's rays to keep the inner gas cells from heating up and expanding. I recognized that this combination of materials constituted a very flammable situation.

I reran the copy of the video the National Archives put together for me time after time, stopping on pause or going through slow motion, sometimes frame by frame. I observed the outer cover on the airship disintegrating rapidly from the obvious hot flames, even around the bottom of the airship. If hydrogen was doing all this, I thought, the Germans found some weird hydrogen!

Chapter 5

The Hindenburg

In July 1900 Count Ferdinand von Zeppelin conducted the maiden flight of the world's first rigid frame airship–the Zeppelin. The trip lasted eighteen minutes and the airship reached a cruising speed of eight miles per hour.

The Zeppelin was one of the great inventions of aviation history and one of the most spectacular and best-loved technological marvels of its age. It became the world's first commercial passenger aircraft. The class of airships known as the Zeppelins initially provided air commercial service in Germany years before airplanes could accommodate fee-paying passengers.

During World War I the Zeppelins carried out the first systematic aerial bombing in the history of war, dropping bombs on London, Paris, and other cities in Europe. New York was considered a possible target. However, the crude navigation tools were too great a problem at the time to consider long distance flights.

In August 1929, Germany's pride and joy, the *Graf Zeppelin* was taken on a voyage around the world. With sixty-one people on board, the great airship flew from New Jersey to Germany, across Siberia, over cheering crowds in Tokyo, across the Pacific Ocean to San Francisco and on to Lakehurst, New Jersey. The trip took twenty-one days and the "Graf" logged over 20,000 miles.

Other nations built rigid airships as well, and to some degree copied the basic Zeppelin designs. The American giant airships such as the *Macon* and *Akron* were built for and flown by the Navy. An earlier airship the *Shenandoah* was in service in 1925. All three of these helium filled airships met their demise during adverse weather conditions. Research indicates that there were also design deficiencies that may have contributed to the disasters.

Probably the worst airship disaster was the British airship designated R101. It met its demise in bad weather conditions, crashed and burned in October 1930 near Paris with 45 of the 48 people on board killed. There are some interesting photos taken after the accident that show the cellulose nitrate/iron-oxide/powdered-aluminum coated envelope completely consumed. I guess for historical accuracy, there appears to be a very small piece of fabric dangling out near the end of the starboard fin.

I have talked with people who have flown on Zeppelins including the *Hindenburg*. To them it was a voyage to contrast with the sea-swaying ocean liners and airplanes in which the only scenery was clouds at 35 thousand feet. The giant airships traveled just a few hundred feet above the land or sea allowing passengers to see the terrain and other marvels along the way. The motion was almost undetectable. One person I talked to, Hal Dick, a passenger on many flights, made the point that he would place a fountain pen on end on the dinning tabletop and it would remain that way during the trip. The airship would go from Europe to the US in less time than the ocean liner.

The *Hindenburg* could maneuver around storms and basically wait until conditions at landing were favorable with no worries about running out of fuel or provisions, considering the large storage areas it had. Passengers had luxury accommodations, a dining area, and could freely move about to gaze at the villages below with the soft rumble of the engines in the background. Not that way in an airplane!

The air traveler of today, squeezed into a narrow seat, meals deposited on a small tray in front of them, would look with envy at the spacious accommodations provided in an airship. In the cramped aisles on the airplane, passengers wait while the fight attendant moves the food-serving cart to allow passing. Then there is "little Jeffrey" a few seats away crying and yelling all the way, until landing when he is finally sound asleep! His mom does not have the luxury of going to a private cabin like on the *Hindenburg*. On the airplane, loud jet engines prevent travelers seated next to each other from carrying on an intelligible conversation. By contrast, in the *Hindenburg*, passengers sat at a lavishly appointed table discussing topics in a normal tone of voice.

The *Hindenburg* was the 118th Zeppelin built. It carried the shop number of 129 or LZ-129. LZ stood for the Luftschiffbau Zeppelin Company. There had been ten designs before 129 but they were not built for a number of reasons. For example, the airship's first design was number 128. It was a smaller design than 129 and was to be used exclusively in hydrogen service. But the decision was made to design the 129 using both helium and hydrogen. Thus the LZ-128 "idea" was scrapped.

The mighty 804-foot long, LZ-129, was fifteen stories high. The gas cells were doughnut shaped with an axial passageway in the center running the length of the airship. Originally the design drawings show a set of sixteen dual gas cells. Each would have an inner cell for hydrogen encapsulated by an outer cell for helium. The intent was to use and preserve the heavier and expensive helium for static lift, and use the lighter and cheaper hydrogen for venting and trim purposes.

Let us visit the topic of buoyancy so misunderstood by many people. The so-called "lift" is based on Archimedes' principle; namely, that a body, wholly or partly immersed in a fluid, is buoyed up with a force equal to the weight of the fluid displaced by the body. The resultant upward force is called the buoyancy of the immersed body. Thus a boat on the water has a buoyancy potential of the amount, actually the weight, of the water it displaces. But if the boats weight with its cargo exceeds the buoyancy "potential" it will sink.

Likewise for an airship, or balloon, the buoyancy potential is a function of the amount, again the weight or density of air it displaces. One has to factor in the weight of the airship along with all its appurtenances, cargo, people, and so forth. If the difference in weight is positive then the airship will "float" or rise.

Obviously the larger the airship the more air it will displace. Now there is the mechanical problem of keeping the air displaced and at the same time keeping the air outside the airship. In the case of the boat, it is constructed of a waterproof and strong hull to withstand the outside water pressure. The airship has an outer cover called the envelope. This "skin" must be able to withstand the air pressure and at the same time prevent air intrusion through the skin.

But how can one keep the skin from collapsing?

By filling the "balloon" with another gas that is less dense than air.

This was the design of early airships. For a number of reasons this was changed to where the airship still retained the outer envelope but had a number of gas "bags" or cells inside.

It became necessary for the LZ-129 gas cell design to be

modified for 100% hydrogen, since the United States was unwilling to sell helium to Germany, in view of Adolf Hitler's war movements across Europe and the prospects of the airship being used for military reasons. As we will see later in this chapter maybe that was not the real reason.

Powered by four, 1,000 horsepower engines, LZ-129 also had two small Diesel engines installed in the hull to drive generators supplying current for lighting, heating, cooking and air conditioning. Unlike any previous Zeppelin, the LZ-129 had two decks. The lower deck contained the kitchen, a mess for officers, and a special designed smoking-room with walls of golden yellow leather. The dining room and bar, a lounge, writing and reading-room and passenger cabins were located on the upper deck. Promenades ran down the sides of the hull, with windows providing a view.

In the winter of 1936/1937, because of not using the heavier helium, the cabin area was expanded from 50 passengers to hold 72. Much attention was paid to space and décor and the lounge was equipped with an aluminum Bluthner baby grand piano. First time a baby grand was brought on board an airship.

Based on previous airship accidents, much attention to safety was inherent in the LZ-129 design. The engines ran on diesel fuel, rather than the more volatile gasoline or light fuel gas as used on the Graf. The gas cells were made using a celluloid sheet sandwiched between cotton fabric and treated with gelatin and latex coatings. This was a vast improvement over the "goldbeater's" design in which cattle gut linings were stitched to a fabric. Called goldbeater's skin because it was used by artisans to contain gold as they hammered it into gold leaf. The result was to significantly reduce the permeation of hydrogen through the gas cell walls by an order of magnitude.

The air space between the cells and envelope included inlets at the hull bottom and a very efficient hooded vent system at the top. This allowed even the smallest amount of "trapped" hydrogen, and that is all it would be, from accumulating within the hull.

Another major design change was to change the highly flammable cellulose- nitrate and/or acetate-based doping of the envelope, typical of previous airships, to one containing a butyl acid. This was to reduce the flammability of the outer cover. Only the upper surface of the airship was first coated with the iron oxide, to reduce the sun's rays from heating up the internal gas cells, as compared with the R 101 in which the entire airship was first coated with the oxide. Powdered aluminum was used in the doping (paint) chemistry. This addition helped reflect the sun's rays.

All in all, the doping processes and materials used on the airships were the best combination in the industry at the time. The formulation made the envelope taught, with better aerodynamics, weather resistant, and increased the life of the fabric. At the time much experimental work had taken place to incorporate flame-retardants into the paint formula, but these failed primarily due to the affect the chemicals had on the doped fabric. The finished paint surface cracked and peeled in these experiments.

Thus the best, and optimum, technology known at the time was incorporated in the construction of the spectacular *Hindenburg*.

The *Hindenburg* was not the last large airship built. The LZ-130 (*Graf Zeppelin II*) was built (same size as the *Hindenburg*) and began trial flights in September 1938. As author J. Duggan put it, "With engines throttled back so that there was almost no sound to be heard, the 'Graf Zeppelin' flew in a great arc over the city and was easily visible from all quarters. The huge silver body of the ship floated quietly and safely in the wonderful autumn sky. Only the swastika on the tail fins provided a speck of colour in the powerful, shimmering body of the colossus. If anywhere the word 'majestic' is used, then the sight of this great new airship must justify it." *LZ 130 "Graf Zeppelin" 1996.*

* * *

Colleague Richard Van Treuren set up an opportunity for me to take a ride on the Fuji airship. We flew over Daytona Beach and part of the Atlantic Ocean. We could see the sharks swimming near the shoreline. It was a very smooth ride. My wife remarked how the seats were better than first class on an airliner and the visibility was really something. There was lots of room to roam around. The pilot let me take over the co-pilot position to get a feel of handling the airship. I was used to handling a large twin-screw boat and the feel of the delay for the boat to react to the controls. The airship was the same except that in addition to steering left and right one has to "steer" up and down at the same time. I could actually carry on a conversation with the low hum of the engines.

The pilot was Scott Danneker who would become the pilot of the new Zeppelin, the NT. He had two interesting remarks. One was when people used to approach him before getting on an airship they would ask, "Is it filled with hydrogen?" Now they ask about what kind of paint is used to cover the airship. The other point that he makes is he is getting tired of documentary stories showing the *Hindenburg* fire. "What would happen if people felt compelled to mention Pan Am flight 103 every time they talked about airplanes?" PA 103 was a major airline disaster.

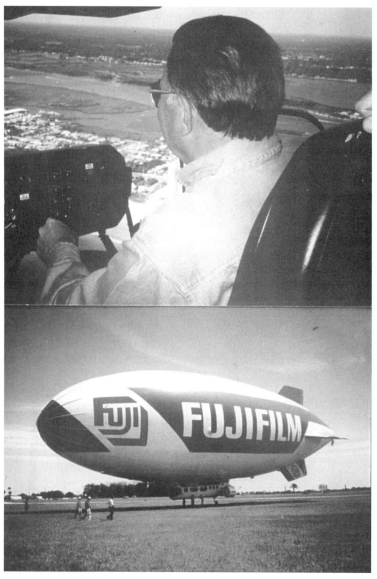

Fuji Airship

The safety record of airship travel is actually quite good. From 1908 to 1937 the Zeppelins racked up over 440 billion passenger miles. Only thirteen passengers did not arrive safely

(*Hindenburg*). The *Schwaben*, *Viktoria Luise*, *Hansa* and *Sachen* made 760 flights in a period of three years and carried 14,000 passengers without mishap.

Various organizations worldwide are trying to reawaken interest in airship travel. Airships hold many advantages, not just for the purpose of carrying passengers, but can do things airplanes and helicopters cannot do. For example the ideas of carrying large generators or oil drilling equipment to remote sites, reducing barge traffic on the Mississippi, fighting forest fires with aerial retardants, launching rockets or bombs from high altitudes, and terrorist surveillance, are just a few that have been proposed.

The special nonflammable property of helium led to its application in dirigibles in the early years. Interest in large-scale helium production was spawned by the US interest in large airships.

As mentioned, initially the LZ-129 design incorporated helium filled gas cells in conjunction with hydrogen filled gas cells. The US—the only viable helium supplier—decided not to sell it to Germany. The US reasoned that the Germans would use the airships for military means. That was really foolhardy as the Zeppelin Company was going to build and fly their airships anyway, of course using hydrogen. So there must have been more to the politics than was being admitted.

I found out that Pan American Airways (PAA) exerted pressure to hinder the export of helium to Germany and so undermine the competitive threat posed by the airships. Despite the fact that the US Postal Service paid more for a pound of mail by airplane than by airship, US legislation in 1937 discriminated against the airship (US Foreign Air Mail Act of 1937). There was suspicion that the US Post Office, closely associated with PAA, had a hand in perpetuating a handicap for the German airship, which was the only one in prospect. So it has been said the American company would bring every possible pressure to bear in an attempt to hinder, if not cripple, the competition from German airships for the transatlantic carriage of mail and possibly passengers. Perhaps it was not strategic and military concerns that denied helium supplies to Germany, but the competition for emerging air routes across the Atlantic, as we will see next.

Looking through the May 1937 (the month of the *Hindenburg* disaster) issues of *The New York Times,* there are some interesting related articles on the status of airline activities of the time. United Airlines offers a New York to Chicago 4 hour and 45 minute nonstop flight at a rate of $44.95, and another 100 bucks gets you to LA, San Francisco or Seattle.

May 10, 1937, Glenn Martin Co. announced plans to build an aircraft assembly plant in which they would be able to build wingspans of up to 290 feet. May 16, Dick Merrill and sidekick Jack Lamble complete first round-trip transatlantic flight in a two- engine Lockheed *Electra,* with claims in three years there would be routine flights between Europe and the US. May 20, a new type of flying boat being worked on near London designed specifically for transatlantic flight. May 25, Pan American Airline flies the *Bermuda Clipper,* 783 miles from New York to Bermuda.

Clearly the emerging airline industry would compete with airship travel, despite the luxury, despite the controlled availability of helium.

* * *

There is a flaw in many peoples' thinking regarding helium versus hydrogen use in an airship. The most common argument made by airship aficionados is that there is a 7% disadvantage using helium because it is denser. The problem is far more complex. Helium weighs twice as much, therefore the first obligation of helium over hydrogen is to lift *itself*. The weight of an airship is not subject to drastic change, so substituting helium for hydrogen in an airship designed for hydrogen greatly reduces the only thing that could be changed—the payload.

The operation of a hydrogen filled airship results in a blow-off of about 2% of the gas when rising to operational altitude. For a helium airship, blow-off is out of the question. To compensate, the cells are not completely filled, further decimating their payload capabilities. The differences in on-board engine fuel requirements (to get the equivalent range) also add to the equation. Airship guys like C. Burgess and P. Teed, who have written papers on this topic, calculate that the airship's useful load is decreased by 31%, and the loss of commercial load is an astonishing 59%.

Thomas Slate, inventor of an all-metal airship, was pushing his idea of a nonflammable airship, but he still needed hydrogen. He stated that if he used helium he would lose the 37,000 pounds of lifting power afforded by hydrogen or virtually the entire payload of the airship.

The most common argument made by the public for helium vs. hydrogen is the relative safety of helium. An interesting analysis by colleague Van Treuren shows a comparison of the experiences of the British hydrogen filled SS airships with the American helium filled K airships.

SS airships	K airships
158 built	134 built
8 lost to fire	12 lost to fire

The fires were started because of one problem or another with the engine fuel.

When I give my presentation at conferences on my *Hindenburg* research, it involves about 120 slides. The last two slides are what gets everyone's attention. Next to the last slide, I show an airship on fire. The fire started because dumped fuel on the ground found an ignition source (1956 at Glynco NAS airship ZSG2-1). I point out that the airship is conveniently moored to the mast, that it is raining, and that the fire fighting crews are busy spraying water on the fire. The next, and final slide, shows the situation about 15 seconds later. The envelope is gone! I then close the presentation with, "Ladies and gentleman that airship was filled with helium."

Sad to say the helium did little to snuff out the fire.

The fire at Glynco

Chapter 6

That Day At Lakehurst

The New York Times headlines on the May 6, 1937 first edition goes something like this: "Bordeaux-Marseilles express is bombed with a combination explosive and infernal machine," "The Young Communist League goes on record pushing for a 30-hour work week, vacation with pay, freedom of press and seek federal dollars for educational facilities." Ads indicate Sax 5th Avenue is having a sale on gold watches for $18.75, a quart of Four Roses rye whiskey is $3.22 and a new Ford V-8, 60 HP Coupe is going for $529.

The 63rd flight of LZ-129 from Frankfurt am Main, Germany to Lakehurst, New Jersey was scheduled for May 1937. Sixty-one crewmembers and 36 passengers were on board, plus mail, cargo, luggage and two dogs. While the outbound ride was only half-booked, all places were sold for the return trip. Many who had reserved the $400 tickets were Americans who wanted to be in London on May 12th to attend the coronation of King George VI.

After a successful trip to Rio for the first flight of the 1937 season, the *Hindenburg* departed Frankfurt, Germany for the first link to Lakehurst, New Jersey on Monday, May 3, 1937. Because of unfavorable head winds encountered en route to the US, the scheduled arrival time of 7 AM (Eastern Daylight Savings Time) was deferred to 7 PM the same day, May 6, 1937.

During the afternoon of May 6, cumulonimbus and cumulus clouds developed locally and a cold front moved slowly over the air station. Several heavy showers occurred between 6 and 7 PM with accompanying thunder. The storm was moving north and it was expected that by the time the airship arrived, the storm would have moved away from the air station. The airship circled south of the station for conditions to improve and get the OK for landing.

Conditions at the time of approach were: ceiling 2,000 to 3,000 feet; very light rainfall; signs of clearing to the west; barometric pressure 29.72; temperature 60 deg F; relative humidity 98%; surface wind light, variable and shifting. The wind at the top of the weather tower (96 feet) was west 6 knots. Occasional lightning was visible in the south and southwest, but none at the field at the time of landing. The airship approached the field from the southwest.

The attempted landing made on this occasion has been described as a high landing or flying mooring, a favorite technique of the US Navy, but unorthodox for most of the *Hindenburg* landings. According to George Watson, a Navy Officer, the "Flying Moor" procedure had been practiced at Lakehurst during the 1936 season (landings at the other five sites in Germany and Brazil were conventional). Doing this during a highly charged atmosphere (thunderstorm conditions) was probably not the thing to do. Airships can accumulate a very high static charge on the hull. The Germans preferred to approach the landing party close to the ground so the lines could be taken in hand and the airship walked up

Courtesy C. Ganz/B. Schneider collection

LZ-129, May 6, 1937

to the mast and be secured. Unbeknown to many, the charge would be less.

The altitude of the airship was about 180 feet above the ground. It rose to 200 feet, at which point the bow port landing rope checked its rise. Thereafter, it descended to about 150 feet. The bow port 2 inch diameter manila trail rope had been coupled with the ground winch system. The bow starboard trail rope was being handled by the landing party in preparation to coupling with the winch. The main bow steel cable had been let out about 50 feet but never reached the ground. The airship was still 700 feet from the mooring mast. The 413-foot long bow ropes had been let out at 7:21 PM. The airship was stationary, and then a light gust of wind shifting from port side began to swing it to starboard.

The gas cells could be vented from the control car as a group or individually. Venting cells 3 through 14 could be done simultaneously and was called, "Valving at the wheel." Cells 1 and 2, as well as cells 15 and 16 were interconnected and each set was controlled by a separate mechanism. Officer Bauer testified that the only valving during the trip prior to landing was near Nova Scotia. Officer Ziegler indicated the highest elevation was about 1,400 meters in an attempt to go over a storm situation.

A review of the airship log shows the airship was typically at 200 to 350 meters in altitude except for one time at 1,400 meters, 41 hours out of Frankfurt.

The significance of this log entry is that all the gas cells had to be vented in view of the temperature and barometric pressure changes from the airship status at Frankfurt, and of course the change in altitude. The data, along with the gas cell design information, allowed me to calculate the amount of hydrogen vented. This analysis was important for me to understand the probable status of the stern cells, particularly cells 1 and 2, at the time of landing. Further discussion about these cells and their probable role in the accident will be addressed later.

From the air station perspective, a fire was observed breaking out at the upper stern area of the airship at 7:25 PM or about four minutes after the release of the two bow ropes.

The difficulty in describing the disaster is well-summarized in the Air Commerce Bulletin report, "Numerous expert and lay witnesses on the field testified as to where they first observed the fire on the airship. There was great diversity in this testimony for reasons that are very apparent. Among the most important of these reasons was the extreme rapidity with which the fire spread, the different positions of the witnesses with respect to the ship, the size of the ship, more than one-sixth of a mile in length, and an overall height equivalent to a 15-story building, and the fact that at the time of the fire it was still daylight. It was estimated that the interval between the first glimpse of flame and the impact of the main body of the ship with the ground was 32 seconds. The great majority of the ground witnesses who testified as to the first appearance of fire were at the port side of the ship."

A letter dated May 12, 1937 from a Carl Artner to the board said, "I discovered a flame at the tail of the ship and a few seconds later I heard the first explosion which was followed by two or three more." Artner was next to Hanger One, port side of the airship.

In a news article of May 8th, Mrs. Sallinger is quoted, "At first a sheet of flame shot like fireworks from the tail. We thought it was some sort of signal. And then came the first explosion. A moment later the second blast sent a sheet of flame tearing through the shining hull, the casing seeming to fly off." She was at the spectator fence, also on the port side.

Helmsman Helmut Lau was in the lower stern and first witnessed a sound. Then, looking up, he saw reflection forward and starboard of cell 4. "At first, red and yellow and there was smoke in it. Then cell 4 disappeared, then 3 and 5. Then he felt a strong detonation."

Elizabeth Tobin, resident at the air station, was positioned on the starboard side and indicated seeing a small flame in back of the fin at first, "Saw-toothed and orange colored."

Kenneth Heinrick, former naval officer, recalled hearing one of the engines backfiring just before the fire.

Asbury Park Press news correspondent, Carl Kempf, reported his experience as follows:

"POOFF a mass of flames burst from the rear of the silvered structure about 100 feet from the stern fins. POOFF another burst of flames about the middle of the craft and then the stern started to settle."

Joann Lynch from Monroe, New Jersey had this to say in

her letter to me, "As a child, I had seen the Hindenberg (sic) going South overhead. There was a roar, and a blaze from *behind* (emphasis by author) the tail fins. As closely as I could discern, she tipped slightly with the nose in the air. The flames were yellow-orange."

Len Knowles from Saint Louis, Missouri, expert in metallurgy and thermodynamics, wrote a nice letter outlining the possible chemical reactions involved in the fire. Of note he indicated, "The heat would produce orange to red colors above about 1400 deg F (non black-body radiation). The heat and flames would make the Carbon glow yellow."

* * *

I met Hal Dick at his place in Wichita, Kansas. At first he said he would not talk to me if I were writing a book. He was tired of helping other people. I told him I was working on my degree in school and my dissertation was going to be on the *Hindenburg* disaster. So he invited me up to his apartment. Hal had been an employee of the Goodyear Company and was on assignment with the Zeppelin Company during the construction of the *Hindenburg* as an advisor. A small man in his late '80's, I recognized him from photos, he was still sporting a crew cut with a flat top. He flew on the *Hindenburg* many times, but not the last flight. An engineer, he was also a balloon pilot and it pleased him to no end to show me his licenses approved by Orville Wright. He was the only one that could explain the two falling tanks shown in the photos seconds after the fire broke out. They were wastewater tanks that were mounted on quick release mechanisms. The idea would be to use them as emergency ballast release, but in this case it was obvious the release was not intentional.

"Why release ballast at that point in time especially in the

Hal Dick with the author.

forward part of the airship? This would only make the bow rise as it did," he observed.

I discussed the witness testimony where there was a jolt through the airship when the rear cells apparently burst out towards the rear.

Hal said, "That might do it."

But he told me he still stuck to the theory of a broken wire breaching a gas cell, but changed his mind over the years as to which wire. His final thought was that it was one of the netting wires around the number four gas cell.

He said, "Where are you coming from, what are your ideas?"

I first accounted my career with NASA and association with hydrogen.

Then I said, "Hal, I am suspicious of the envelope."

"Addison, what you want to do is concentrate on what they did to the 130 (LZ-130). They made a lot of changes especially in the area of reducing static buildup. For example, they stretched the ramie cord and ran it through graphite before using it to tie the panels to the frame."

This procedure would help any charge buildup to dissipate to the frame as the graphite would allow the cord to be conductive. I asked him about the engine changes that had been made from the 129 to the 130. He thought the main reason for the change was the water recovery scheme. This was a technique of capturing the water vapor from the engine exhaust. The primary reason for the design was to recover water to be used for ballast, lost during flight operations. The design may tone down the charged exhaust particulate, especially any "sparks."

"There were probably a number of reasons as it was a very expensive design change to go to the tractor configuration," he went on to say. Historically the propellers were at the rear of the engines and "pushed" the airship. The tractor mode placed the propellers at the front of the engine and therefore pulled like a tractor, thus the designation. This configuration was best for incorporating the water recovery system.

"Do you think that would change the exhaust behavior?" I was probing, following the engine backfire possibility.

The conversation quickly turned to his camera hobby, so that ended the interview.

* * *

Charlie White worked at Paramount Pictures on 44th street in New York City in 1937. We met at his place in Port Orange, Florida. He told me that the film taken at the disaster site was without sound. A copy was sent to him with a narrator on a

The author with Charlie White

Vitaphone record for a voice over, a studio procedure also called sound striping to edit in the desired voice or sound. He was asked to dub in some background sound for the final edit of the film for broadcast. He said that what he used was a recording of a fire that had occurred in Philadelphia, also on a Vitaphone record, that had the sounds of a large fire "booming" and people sounds in the background. We discussed other newsreel accounts. Most takes, he said, used footage from film of flights during 1936. However, what one with a good eye will notice is that the images show the LZ-129 in clear skies along with the Olympic rings painted on the side. The disaster occurred on a rainy day and the rings were removed prior to the 1937 season. Other versions depict horrifying screams and explosions and glass "windows" breaking. The windows of the airship were made of a plastic. So Charlie White, "The Movie Man" as his business card displayed, helped us understand the partially fake newsreels, movies and documentaries of the disaster.

* * *

J. Gordon Vaeth, an airship historian, published his book in 1958, *Graf Zeppelin The Adventures of an Aerial Globetrotter*. We met near where he lives in Olympia, Washington. Over a nice lunch we discussed my research and findings so far. This was September 1997, shortly after the first published account of my work in the Smithsonian *Air and Space* magazine. One comment that he made, I will always remember.

"Addison, when you talk to the people who were there keep in mind that it was an experience many years ago, that over the years their ideas and recollections have been formulated in their minds and are indelible."

He autographed a copy of his book with, "To Add Bain – airship researcher par excellence who may well have discovered the cause of the Hindenburg fire."

* * *

Eugen Bentele was a mechanic on board the final flight of the *Hindenburg*. He was in engine car number four, the one towards the bow on the port side. He had flown on 129 LZ flights, about 50 on the *Hindenburg*. With an interpreter, I interviewed him at his residence in Friedrichshafen, Germany in July, 1996, and again about two years later. Through the Zeppelin museum, I had communicated with Bentele several times on various points of detail since then. He was emphatic about the fact that there was no gasoline on board and that the engines were started by compressed air. This was contrary to

Eugen Bentele with the author.

reports of electrical starting and using gasoline as a starter fluid, like your automobile engine. The crew did have what they called a fuel sprayer. This was used to mist some diesel fuel into the air intake to help start the engine when it was cold. Bentele was very vivid about explaining the very hot fire as he was running away from the burning airship on the ground. He had to pat the back of his head to keep the fire from burning his hair. Although he was some distance from the fire, it was still very intense. I asked what hydrogen smelled like. This point came up several times in the Board of Inquiry deliberations. He pointed to his kitchen stove, on natural gas, and said, "Like that but not exactly, a little different smell."

He did not know if "they" deliberately added an odorant or if that was the way it came from production. He was aware that pure hydrogen did not have an odor. There were four crewmembers in the tail at the time and they did not smell any hydrogen, which would have indicated there was a leak. He indicated that very seldom do you see exhaust particles, maybe at night and when you reverse the engine. I was very interested in the condition of engine number two. He could see it very clearly and at the time it was only in an idle status, with nothing unusual, no backfiring or exhaust stream.

This is consistent with the testimony of Fischer and Deutsche, the mechanics in engine car number two. What is important is to establish the fact that it was engine number one that backfired.

I raised the question about the sabotage theory, the subject of a book written by Hoehling in which he developed a theory that rigger Erich Spehl placed a bomb in the aft section of the airship and then moved to the "safety" of the bow just before landing.

Bentele, a short balding man, very cautious but sharp witted, looked at me and said, "Spehl was a young kid. He was too dumb to know how to build a bomb let alone know where and how to place it."

* * *

Alfred Groezinger was a cook on board the final flight. At his residence just outside Friedrichshafen, we discussed his experience. A tall, soft spoken man with a nice head of gray hair, he was one of three of the twelve-crew members up near the bow that survived. I told him of the literature stating it was necessary to send six members of the crew forward to make up for the heaviness of the tail upon the landing attempt. The practice was not unusual. He said he had done it before.

The author with Alfred Groezinger

Groezinger personally got permission to take Richard Mueller and Fritz Flakus with him, only because these young boys never witnessed a landing with the great view they would have in the bow section. Both boys perished. He did not remember exactly what happened to him. He felt the very hot fire rush over him, then was sort of stunned, after which the bow hit the ground and he could run away. But the intense heat of the fire he could, "Feel for a long way."

He recalled, "Red and yellow like any sort of fire."

I also indicated he had been quoted as saying someone passed by him on the way forward before the fire, complaining there was a problem in the rear of the airship.

"No one talked to me, I talked with the boys but that was it."

John Iannoceone and the author.

He knew nothing about hydrogen odors but had heard, "The mechanics knew about it."

* * *

John Iannoceone was part of the Navy ground crew and was at the scene. I had written John to get his viewpoint in more detail as he had been quoted many times in the newspaper on or around the anniversary of the disaster. I never got a response but had the opportunity to meet with him at Lakehurst in 1999. He told me of his position forward of the bow and was looking up shortly after hearing a sound and saw this "Big red glow inside the airship."

"That's hydrogen burning," he declared.

I responded politely, "I would not dispute you saw the red glow. From your perspective it would make sense, but what you did not see were the events a few seconds before. Hydrogen is colorless if it was burning."

* * *

George Watson was an officer stationed at Lakehurst and was on hand at the time of the *Hindenburg* disaster. In a phone call to him, he told me of the intense heat from the fire and was amazed at how fast the event occurred. He recalled the sounds. More like two loud thumps rather than a true explosion.

* * *

I drove to Pennsauken, New Jersey, to meet with Hank Applegate. He offered to take me out to Lakehurst for a self-guided tour of the facilities. Hank had been the fire chief for a number of years at Lakehurst and was an avid collector of stuff on airships including some *Hindenburg* artifacts, photos and so on. I wanted to get a first hand look at Hanger One and the exact spot where the disaster occurred "that day" at Lakehurst. We spent the day discussing issues with airships. Hank took me to a storage hanger and showed me a pressure valve from a gas cell. The purpose of the valve was to release gas if the pressure rose to a certain limit to protect the gas cell. It was large, about the diameter of my kitchen table. I was keenly interested in how it operated.

At Hanger One, where the *Hindenburg* had been staged on a few occasions, Hank gave me a tour of the interior. The vastness reminded me of the Space Shuttle "hanger." I looked down at the floor of this facility, built in the1920's.

"Hank, it looks like all those bricks fared well over the years," I inquired.

"Those are spark proof. If a worker were to drop a tool on them no spark would be produced." He replied.

I quickly thought it was because of the hydrogen, then paused, thinking that would be overkill in the design. He sort of read my mind. Then this ex-fire chief said, "They use to have a lot of solvents and flammable paints around to make airship repairs. You want a brick?"

"Sure!" I said.

Hank took out his jackknife, bent down and dislodged a brick and handed it to me.

I had a heck of a time explaining to security at the airport on my flight back what I was doing with this dirty brick in my attaché case.

Kevin from the Lakehurst Historical Society joined us.

Hindenburg Memorial

"Addison, lets take a climb to the top of the hanger," he invited me.

So off we went up the many stairwells to the rafters in the ceiling, then across small walkways to get from one side to the other, carefully hanging on to nearby frames of structural steel.

"Whoa, look at that!" I said looking here and there.

Kevin replied, "Yeah, pigeon crap."

It must have been a foot deep in spots. Of course considering the amount of time the birds used the hanger for home, no wonder!

*　*　*

Stanley Washburn was among the ground crew members at the disaster site. He explained about the bright color and concussion in his writings to me. No big bang. He had developed a theory that it was a gas cell level indicator that triggered the event. He related the fact that Anton Wittemann, formerly a commander of the *Graf Zeppelin*, was actually a passenger on the *Hindenburg* flight, but was in the control car at the time of the incident to observe (not participate) in the landing. It was he who Washburn claims pressed the button to get aft cell level readings, thus sparking the fire.

*　*　*

Mary Ritting was parked in a car near the station as the airship was preparing to land. It flew over her. I met with Mary and her son at her home in Hollywood. Her description indicates the event took place in the very aft end of the airship. On her coffee table she oriented items to illustrate her location and vantage point with the airship. I sketched out a drawing of her arrangement and took it home to study later to confirm she witnessed the event from aft/starboard. She gave me a small

The author with Mary Ritting

vase that she acquired that had been sitting on a table in the
Hindenburg at the time of the fire. I will eventually see that the
vase goes to the Smithsonian.

* * *

I visited Robert (Bob) Rutan and his wife, Mary, in
Columbia, Maryland. Bob was the son of Lucius Rutan, an
officer that was on the US airship the *Akron* when it crashed in
April 1933. Young Rutan, then seventeen, was with a friend
near the port/aft engine (car 2). He heard a backfire, looked
up to see the fire, and then ran. Of significance is his recollection
that they detected the smell of gasoline just before the fire.
Thus the backfire producing a spark ignited the gasoline, he
still contends. He showed me a photo out of a book written

The author with Bob Rutan

by mechanic Bentele. The photo shows an interconnect of two fuel tanks, thus suggesting one was for gasoline for prestart of the Diesel engine. Also gasoline was used to conserve the batteries for engine starting, so Bob contended.

* * *

David Collier lived in New Jersey. I made arrangements to visit him as he had some interesting information. His father was an airship crewmember on the US airships. Dave recalls the flights of the *Hindenburg* over their house and the day he got to visit the airship moored at Lakehurst. He had a large collection of newspaper articles on the disaster as well as airframe parts and fabric materials from the airship. One large piece of fabric was a panel section tied to another panel section with ramie cord. A very impressive collection that I wound up purchasing from him. Dave included many of the local newspapers he saved of the disaster. The papers included a lot of detail, some of which I would not find in the accident report or other sources, but which I found valuable as my investigation continued.

Collier Collection

* * *

An interesting ad appearing in the 1937 *New York Times* paper talks of the Bell & Howell personal palm size Filmo 8 full color movie camera, "complete with fast, color-corrected lens, it only costs $49.50 at leading photographic stores everywhere." Too bad someone did not have one at Lakehurst that night. Another *New York Times* ad on May 16 from *Pathegrams* announced offer for sale of 100 feet of 16 mm film footage at $3; and 50 feet of 8 mm film footage at $2 of movies of the *Hindenburg Explodes*. These items were for sale only six days after the investigative board convened...interesting.

Claude Collins of *Pathe News* indicated his camera shot 90 feet of film per minute and the footage he got was 51 feet. That equates to the "infamous" 34 seconds. Some say 32 seconds. However we will see later that Claude missed the first and most important 18 seconds.

There is a great story about the response of the *Chicago Tribune* the night of May 6. By 10:20 PM central time, the paper went to press with a full-page cover story of the disaster, complete with pictures, to get on the street by early morning of the 7th. Something like 950,000 copies—some 100,000 more than normal—were printed. Talk about a quick service to the public!

Chapter 7

Accident Investigation

Immediately after the *Hindenburg* accident two boards of inquiry were established. At the direction of the Secretary of Commerce, a US board was authorized. The Reichsminister of Aeronautics authorized a German investigating commission and the team arrived at Lakehurst on May 13. Both groups independently considered two basic theories: accidental causes and sabotage.

It is very important to note that both investigating teams, in considering the possibility of accidental cause, proceeded down the path that unequivocally hydrogen, and only hydrogen, was the problem. Therefore the teams set out to examine two factors. The US board stated, "There must be present (a) a combustible mixture of hydrogen and oxygen of the air and (b) sufficient heat to ignite such mixture." The question then became one of rationalizing the mechanism of how hydrogen leaked out and then discovering the source of ignition.

The difficulty was to establish the two events simultaneously. The idea was further complicated by the necessity of having a *proper* mix of combustible gas and the *correct* ignition energy at the *precise* location.

The quest was to identify the source of free hydrogen. Cell diffusion, vent valve failure, decreased ventilation, entry of a piece of propeller, fracture of a hull wire (breaching a gas cell) or a major structural failure, were options considered by the Board.

Witness R. H. Ward, in charge of the port bow landing party, testified he saw a fluttering of the outer cover on the port, topside, of cell 5.

"It was a wave motion ... as if gas was escaping."

This observation took on a lot of interest by Dr. Hugo Eckener, the Director of the Zeppelin Company, since loose hydrogen was unequivocally assumed the cause of the disaster.

In the original testimony (page 1199), Gunther Bock, Director, *Deutsche Verersuckanstalt fuer Luftfahrt*, said he thought the fluttering of the outer cover was caused by the air whirls caused by the fire within the ship.

Lt. R. W. Antrim also saw a flutter but "After the port engine... it was very loose and fluttering."

Airship expert H. Dick indicated in his writings that on the first flight of LZ-129, cover flutter was a problem and additional doping or anti-flutter wires were required. The flutter to which he refers was not due to escaping gas, but to the movement of air across the cover during flight.

Commander C.E. Rosendahl, in charge of the Lakehurst Naval Air Station, and an airship officer said, "It seems to me that the fluttering of the cover...could easily have been caused by the passage along the hull of the ship of the light gust of wind which struck the ship on the port side... It is a matter of common knowledge that airship fabric which becomes slack in places in damp weather will flutter."

During my research, I uncovered statements regarding flutter as a routine problem especially when the cover got wet. I also noticed in film footage from a vantage point above and to the port side, almost all panels of the *Hindenburg* were fluttering during flight. Again, this was not from escaping gas, but from the aerodynamics of the flight.

Dr. Eckener testified it would take 40 to 50 cubic meters of gas per second to cause a cover flutter. It is noted in several sources that the gas cell pressure of cell 4 was only one-inch water pressure and the cell volume was down to about 7800 cubic meters as the *Hindenburg* came into Lakehurst. I suggest it would have taken a sizeable opening to support Eckener's statement and the resulting flow (loss of gas) would have been noticed on the control car instrumentation, which it was not.

Watch Officer A. Sammt, in charge of ship trim control, testified he did not notice any drop.

There was much discussion recorded in the testimony about the apparent tail heaviness of the airship just prior to the intended landing. This avenue of discussion was to offer evidence that hydrogen was escaping from the stern, the origin of the fire.

According to Commander Rosendahl, "Had there been an appreciable leakage of hydrogen at the stern, it seems to me that it would have been detected by the gas-pressure instruments in the control car, or by the loss of buoyancy in the stern, a condition which in the existing light wind would have been apparent to the personnel at the instruments and the elevator wheel in the control car. The stern, however, did not drop but actually rose somewhat while the ship hung on the landing ropes." [This could be due to the gas in the cells expanding from the heat and providing lift, temporarily.]

Other accounts indicate that Captain Pruss usually approached the landing mast with the airship in a slight nose up-attitude. Second Officer H. Bauer, provided notes showing an angle of attack (inclination) of 3/4 of a degree positive (up at the bow) just prior to two sequences, one for 15 seconds, then one for 5 seconds, of releasing gas from cell 11 through 16 (forward cells). This action along with dropping of water ballast at frame 77 (stern) brought the airship in trim, while lowering the altitude 30 meters, which it held for six minutes prior to the fire breakout.

Second Officer W. Ziegler, in charge of the valving system and gas level meters in the control car, testified that any gradual loss of gas in the rear cells would have been noticed. He further stated a rigger would hear escaping gas because of its whistling noise and it would have been heard at a distance of at least ten meters. The four crewmen in the stern-fin area reported that no unusual sounds were heard prior to the incident. During the hearing, the crew witnesses were asked if they had smelled any hydrogen, they all reported they did not, but knew it had an odor.

Chief engineer Rudolph Sauter, testified that, "Concerning the gas cells could only say that everything was in the best of order." (page 462 of testimony).

Pure hydrogen is odorless but according to airship writer J. G. Vaeth, a garlic or onion type odorant was used in flammable airship gases.

The idea of a broken wire causing the rent of a gas cell has been the favored theory over the years by airship experts. There is discontinuity, however, whether it was a bracing, tension, shear, axial, diagonal or cell netting wire.

In reading through the extensive literature on airship operations and accident accounts I found no reference to wire breaking and subsequent cell damage. There are accounts of the chafing of a cell with the airships' frame requiring subsequent patching while in flight, but the gas cells on the *Hindenburg* were contained in a network of both ramie cord and steel wire netting to control the movement of the gas cell.

Rosendahl said, "It is known that of the thousands of wires in an airship, once in a while one has failed in flight, but in such cases, even in hydrogen ships, often not even the slightest damage has resulted."

Dr Eckener in his 1937 testimony indicated experiences with broken wires, but not on the *Hindenburg*.

The "sharp turn" at landing is the favorite explanation (putting stress on the network of wires, thus breaking one or more which could puncture a gas cell). I discount that explanation because on March 26, 1936, the mishandled takeoff of the *Hindenburg* in Germany caused significant damage to the lower fin. No one identified any broken wires as a result of that accident. One would tend to believe the stress induced on the stern in the accident should have been greater than stress from a "sharp turn."

In my interview with H. Dick, he mentioned he had gone over this many times as to which structural wiring system may have been at fault. The cells were loose except at the top, thus maybe the cell wire netting/support system at the top was a better one to blame, because the netting touched the cell material.

In searching for an ignition source, mechanical, chemical, thermodynamic, electrical (equipment spark, resonance, inductance) were all considered. Electrostatics (ball lightning, brush discharge, St. Elmo's fire) was also considered. St. Elmo's fire, a common electrostatic phenomenon, became the favorite theory of the ignition source.

Dr. Ludwig Duerr (the airship designer) suggested that although the engine cars and exhaust pipes both point away from the hull the exhaust could have drifted toward the hull when the ship drifted to starboard just before the fire.

Dr. Eckener brought up a counter point. He indicated

the engine exhaust at idle would not exceed 250 degrees and at max rpm it would be not more than 500 degrees. Hydrogen with air will not ignite below 500 to 600 degrees and besides, over the distance the exhaust would have to travel, the exhaust would have cooled.

Although the Boards of Inquiry later concluded that some form of static electricity was involved in the incident, none was seen by any of the witnesses who testified at the inquiry. In 1964, Dr. Douglas H. Robinson, a noted airship historian and writer, met with Professor Mark Heald of Princeton, New Jersey. Heald was at the station with his wife and son and observed the incident but saw an unusual activity before the fire broke out.

As Robinson says, "Heald...undoubtedly saw St. Elmo's fire flickering along the airship's back a good minute before the fire broke out."

An account is noted of a witness reporting a "real light bluish" indication from starboard, aft. Witness Kirkman alludes to a neon-type light of activity from his starboard vantage point at 400 yards distance, but tended to characterize this observation as a tiny match flame that smoldered prior to the breakout of the flames.

There was much discontinuity regarding the exact location of the beginning of the fire.

Dr. Eckener put a lot of credence on Helmut Lau's observation. Lau was in the lower fin, heard a sound, and then looked up to see the fire above cell 4.

Dr. Eckener testified regarding Lau's statements, " I think that, that was the second stage of the process of burning. Lau could, from his position at the time, not look vertically to the top of the ship through the gas shaft. He could only look forward (toward cell 4) and up at an angle, and he could have

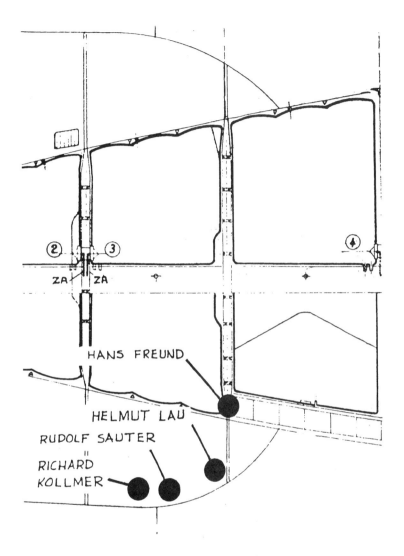

Crewmembers lower fin

only noticed something of the fire as the flames beat down into the gas cell, and if I remember correctly as to what Mr. Lau said, that practically simultaneously with noticing the reflection of fire through the lower part of the gas cell, the total gas cell was consumed. That therefore must have been the moment when the fire burning on top destroyed the top part of the cell and caused the escape of gas" (page 886 of transcript).

Not in the testimony but in a newspaper account, Eckener concludes that the origin of the fire was above the region of cell1 and 2. Cell 1 and 2 were interconnected, so gas from one could flow to the other.

Sabotage was examined under two classifications: the first, external—including the use of incendiary bullet, high-powered electric ray and the dropping of ignition composition from an airplane; the second, internal–including the placement within the ship of a bomb or other infernal device. In view of the large number of people present at the time of the accident, and the fact that there were no reports of any unusual activity, any external cause was dismissed. Both investigating commissions and other experts investigated the accident site for suspicious clues. The surviving crewmembers were thoroughly questioned as to whether they had noticed anything out of the ordinary in this connection.

Since the disaster, a number of movies, books and articles have been published in an attempt to dramatize the execution of an act of violence. However, to date, no physical proof has been offered, only subjective ideas to form the basis of the particular story line. I would suggest these theories are technically flawed, contain misquotes from the original testimony of record, and don't fully connect with the timing of the accident.

I have discussed the timing aspect with the FBI, NASA security and other law enforcement entities. Typical terrorist behavior would appear inconsistent with the circumstances at the time of the accident. The placement of a device in a cell of almost pure hydrogen (not flammable) is not logical. The placement of a device, say near an engine fuel tank is logical but does not equate to the location of the first sign of fire some distance from the tanks.

Books written by Michael Mooney and A. A. Hoehling have based their sabotage theory on a bomb or infernal device placed in, on, or near cell 4, the location of the first sign of fire by crewmember Lau. Also germane to the argument is the sound Lau reported hearing prior to looking up at cell 4. The interrogator, Major Schroeder, asks Lau (page 423 of transcript):

"What was your impression of the detonation..."

Lau said, "More like a kitchen gas range..."

"More on the order of a pop?" asked Schroeder.

"More of a frwump. It was not a sharp detonation," said Lau.

Author, Hoehling, in his book, *Who Destroyed the Hindenburg?* Turned the testimony around to support his bomb theory, claiming Lau described the noise as a "pop." On page 107 of Hoehling's book there are serious misquotes from crewmembers Sauter and Kollmer as well. Hoehling, like many others, concentrated on cell 4, perhaps not knowing of Dr. Eckener's conclusion that the fire's origin was above the interconnected cells, 1 and 2.

It was over 51 years (September 16, 1988) before the 337-page FBI report was declassified regarding the FBI role in the investigative effort into the circumstances surrounding the disaster. The report, in substance, centered on the topic of sabotage.

South Trimble, Jr. was Chairman of the Department of Commerce's Investigative Board corresponding with John Edgar Hoover, Director of the FBI.

Correspondence within the report indicates that the FBI was not called in unless there was a specific aspect to investigate at the request of the Board of Inquiry. The FBI took the stance that it was not their investigation. Even though that was the official position, there was some internal misunderstanding. Special agent in charge, W. Devereaux, sent a cablegram to J. Edgar Hoover on May 19 that he was on his way to Lakehurst. Hoover scrawled across the cablegram to another agent, "Find out what he is going there for. I understand from Connelly that we had tactfully withdrawn from this case." E. J. Connelly was the FBI inspector who attended the hearings on behalf of Hoover.

A sampling of the many letters and communications to the FBI include:

"In view of the fact the Hindenburg was insured for $5,750,000, and that the Hitler government was short of funds, it is possible that the disaster was caused by a Hitler agent, acting on Hitler's orders."

To FBI Director: "Dear Sir, Do you want to know who shot down the dirigible Hindenburg in New Jersey? It was police Lieut of detectives, Ralph De Marteni New York City police dept. He shot it, and with a maxim silencer gun, by order of mayor La Guardia, New York city. Mr. Hoover, search Lieut De Marteni's house, for the gun. Mr. Hoover, its true." [sic]

Another letter states; "The Hindenburg was destroyed by a clock work time fire bomb. This was all planned weeks before. The purpose was to obtain helium. It was not intended to destroy passengers by it but because, of 2 hours delay to make mooring plan was upset. Had mooring been on right time all but 3 or 4 crew also all passengers away and maybe no lives lost at all. Lehman placed bomb aft 4:30 – 5 o'clock P.M time to go about 7 P.M. No other on ship knew of bomb or the plan. Eckner did. He had got Berlin O.K. Some of aft flames showed color chemical used. Perhaps metal near stern now will show different heat flame marks where Lehman set bomb, not sure, but worth looking for. Eckner said he would have helium sure, said this last Feb. don't let him." [sic]

A Mr. Beck from Philadelphia, stating, in substance, that he was quite sure he saw a flash from an airplane that flew over some minutes before the *Hindenburg* landing; that he cannot be certain about the flash, but it looked so to him, and that a bullet shot from that plane into the tail end of the ship might have caused the explosion.

A letter from Trimble to Hoover, subject matter: Passenger Joseph Spaeh, acrobat, who had dogs in the stern area that he had to visit frequently. He was not accompanied by a crewmember, as normal policy, suggesting Spaeh could have access to a rear cell and place a bomb. Trimble continues, "The innuendo of the entire matter is that this acrobat could have climbed out on the motor gondola, removed the cover on the exhaust pipe of the motor, and allowed the flames to set fire to the fabric and explode the hydrogen." The FBI investigated this aspect quite thoroughly but found no evidence suggesting Spaeh had anything to do with the incident. Spaeh wrote a letter to the commission on May 29 delineating his presence at the time of the fire and declaring his innocence.

Erich Spehl was a rigger on the flight, and his last position was at the bow of the airship at the time of the incident. It was said he was a quiet sort of individual and a suspect as well by the crew. If he had anything to do with a device in the stern, obviously staying at the bow would be a good location upon landing. There is nothing in the FBI report about this individual. I talked with surviving crewmembers about Spehl. There is speculation within the airship historian community that it may have been him that made a statement about the gas cells before he went forward to the bow. A crewmember told me nothing was said. Another crewmember, a mechanic, told me basically Spehl wouldn't have the brains to build a bomb let alone know where to put it.

Chairman Trimble furnished the FBI all the letters from passengers, eyewitnesses, and persons who claimed to have observed the flight of the *Hindenburg*, and opinions concerning the possible causes of the disaster. A review of these letters and correspondence indicated that about 30% of them appear to place the responsibility for the disaster upon mechanical defects, 50% upon static discharges and other aerial causes, and about 20% upon possible sabotage perpetrated by Jews and directed against the Hitler regime in Germany.

* * *

There were a number of scientific aspects of the investigation. One was the plaster cast of footprints of two men taken inside the perimeter fence where spectators were not to be. No conclusion was reached. No spent gun shells were found at the location. A yellow substance was found on one of the gas cell valve covers. Sulfur, as used in explosives, was suspected, but the FBI lab found it was not sulfur and more than likely was a residue from burning materials of the airship. Several pieces of frame were examined for traces of nitrate, an explosive ingredient, but nothing was confirmed.

In 1960, author A. A. Hoehling sent a galley copy of the book he was working on to Hoover. His book, *Who Destroyed The Hindenburg?* was based on the sabotage theory. The conclusion of the FBI: "The book is a fictionalized, blow-by-blow account of the last flight of the Zeppelin, Hindenburg. It put forth the theory that the giant dirigible was sabotaged by exploding a photographic flashbulb inside a hydrogen gas cell. This conclusion, however, is pure speculation. The book contains nothing to prove any such occurrence. Since this work puts forth a speculative, unproven theory concerning the Hindenburg disaster and since we furnished relatively little assistance to the author, it would be most unwise for the Bureau to comment in any way concerning this book."

And in the FBI conclusion, File no. 70-396:

"Files of the Investigative Board of the Department of Commerce relative to Hindenburg disaster failed to reflect any information of value upon which an investigation by the Bureau might be reasonably warranted in connection with any possible sabotage or other Federal violations within the investigative jurisdiction of the Bureau, June 17, 1937."

The sabotage theory was dismissed by the Board due to lack of evidence.

However, for the record, let's take a look at the bomb and gunshot ideas and see if it leads us anywhere.

First of all, placing a device like a bomb inside the hydrogen filled cell would do nothing but tear a hole in it–no explosion, no fire, just a hole and a disappointed saboteur! If I were to do it based on the technology of explosives and the knowledge of airships in 1937, I would place a bomb *next* to the cell, and then another timed to go off seconds later at the top of the ship. Might work. Better yet, place the bomb on one of the diesel fuel tanks to really get things going. The problem of putting a bomb on board would be one of timing. Using a preset device, the disaster would have occurred maybe over New York or maybe south of Lakehurst, because of the delays of the trip and landing attempts. Without a timed device, the saboteur would have had been on board to light the fuse, or push the button and consider suicide. The bomb setup didn't happen because the four crewmembers, in close proximity to each other and the only ones in the stern and within sight of the fire's first events, escaped with out a scratch.

Now let's take a look at the gunshot idea. My colleague, Van Treuren, likes to tout this quote: "Viewers of the motion picture, *The Rocketer*, were kept on the edge of their seats as the FBI agent character shouted, 'Watch out for that Zeppelin! It's full of hydrogen! One bad shot and we'll all fry!'"

Gunfire has often been blamed either directly or indirectly in the *Hindenburg* fire.

The FBI report included a letter of a claim of an eyewitness who saw someone take three shots at the airship over New York. A resident of Barnegat Light, New Jersey, for many years, bragged he hated the Nazis so much he had shot LZ-129 with his .306 rifle and his bullet lead to the disaster.

There are many interesting stories concerning attempts to knock down airships with gunfire. During WW I, a number of bullets were designed that were either incendiary, tracer or explosive and all intended to "blow up" the hydrogen filled airships. The ammunition was named for their inventors, Brock, Pomeroy and Buckingham. The problem was, the glowing bullet did not contact the flammable fabric upon entry for a long enough time to transfer enough heat energy to produce ignition. Inside the gas cell, pure hydrogen gas won't support combustion. The best hope for a fire was the exit point, but fleeting tracer rounds were not effective against gasbags even as the bullets left a ragged exit wound.

As one pilot stated, "The German Airship L12 was so badly shot up she settled into the sea, also the German WW I Airship the L19 so severely shot up over Holland she ditched in the North Sea. There was no fire, nor rescue, the crew all drowned. I flew to 800 feet below it from bow to stern and distributed one drum of new Brock and Pomeroy. It seemed to have no effect. I expended another 47-round drum along the side of the Zep with no effect, but with a third drum concentrated the fire on one spot and got a fire started."

There is the story about the L32 attacked by British Lt. Sowery, "I fired at it. The first two drums of ammunition had apparently no effect, but the third one caused the envelope to catch fire in several places." Note the envelope caught fire. Also note the difficulty of causing a problem even with incendiary devices, let alone a common, single, lead bullet.

Another L-class airship story with a different outcome was the airship L49. It was downed to the ground due to enough loss of lifting gas. The crew wasted so much time firing flare pistols into the hydrogen cells in a vain attempt to scuttle their airship that the French soldiers were able to capture them with their Zeppelin still intact!

Since my research went public, I've gotten a number of letters or emails on the subject of sabotage. During December 2001, I received one where someone claimed a friend of a family member shot the *Hindenburg* while in New Jersey.

I had some discussion with the security people at NASA and the FBI at Quantico, Virginia, about sabotage. I read up on the subject with textbooks, *Criminal Investigation*, by Swanson, Chamelin and Territo as well as the same title by Axelrod and Antinozzi and *Crime Science* by Nickell and Fischer.

The issue of sabotage points most to the motives and typology of an arsonist. The key factors along with the motive include opportunity, ability, accessibility and for building a case, the existence of evidence. Lets look at these topics.

From the dozen or so categories suggested by the authors about revenge, I concluded political or terrorist justifications seem more likely. But in all the Board of Inquiry transcripts, FBI transcripts, and interviews I conducted, no one has been able to identify someone of this character on board the airship. Motive is therefore questionable.

Opportunity. There was the opportunity to place a device somewhere but there is the question of timing. The flight was unexpectedly delayed many hours. The crewmembers were constantly looking over the airship status and didn't notice anything unusual.

Ability. The person would need to understand the nature of the device and have a good working knowledge of airships in order to know where to effectively place the device. Inside of a gas cell is not the answer. On top of a fuel tank, maybe, but tests revealed no evidence from any type of explosive device.

Accessibility. The person would need to be a crewmember to be able to get to the very aft of the airship. The four members in the lower fin did not seem to be of suicidal nature. The upper part of cell 1 and 2 (fire origin) is really not accessible from the interior.

Evidence. The FBI as well as the investigative board found nothing suggesting a device-oriented cause of the fire. The criminal investigative textbooks indicate that it is not unusual for the timer used in arsons to actually survive the fire. Research revealed that in most cases an accelerant is used. Nothing of this nature was found. In sabotage-based books about the *Hindenburg,* the idea of the photo flash bulb as the bomb is provided. I recall reading where someone suggested it could be the oxygen inside the bulb to mix with the hydrogen to set things off. What a bunch of nonsense.

The *Hindenburg* was sabotaged? I don't think so.

Case closed. Move on.

* * *

Some people claim equipment failure as a possible cause to the *Hindenburg* accident. We do need to look at some of those ideas.

There is the Washburn indicator spark theory. Stanley Washburn still claims his idea of the gas cell level-indicator system was at fault. The instrument in the bottom of the gas cell sends the signal to the instrument panel in the control car. The claim is when Captain Anton Wittemann in the control car hit the button to get a gas level reading in gas cell 4, a spark occurred at the rheostat in the gas cell.

I don't buy this theory. For starters, why would Wittemann, a passenger, an observer and not a crewmember, do this? Secondly, the rheostat was in almost pure hydrogen and as I've already stated pure hydrogen won't burn. Thirdly, the fire did not start at cell 4. The Zeppelin Company did test the same design just in case, and found no reason not to use it on the LZ-130, the airship built after the *Hindenburg*.

There is the Rutan gasoline theory. Bob Rutan and I talked about this at length. He still claims he smelled gasoline while he was near engine car number 2. His theory–the engine backfired and ignited the gasoline. He showed me a photo out of mechanic Bentele's book. He pointed out the interconnect of two tanks. His claim was that one tank contained diesel fuel and the other gasoline, and that the gasoline was a starter fuel for the engine. At the time, his theory had some credibility. I went on to investigate, contacting the Zeppelin museum, and through them, Bentele. What I learned was that the engines were started with compressed air. There was no gasoline onboard. The "interconnect" was a temporary mode for initial break in of the engines. Oil did accumulate in the "bilge" of the engine car and was occasionally dumped overboard. I am sure that seventeen year-old Rutan did smell something at the time and that the event is "burned" into memory.

* * *

There is the University of Delaware sparking wire theory. This "recent discovery" is backed up by modern forensic science. "One new idea to me is that a cable snapped and caused a spark that may have ignited the hydrogen in the airship" says investigator Rick Hall. Now folks put aside your spectrograph and electron microscope and think about this. Imagine an airship almost three football fields in length, fifteen stories high with many miles of wires and cables of varying size running axially, running horizontally, vertically, diagonally and every which way throughout the airship. The airship was essentially stationary four minutes before the fire broke out. The *Hindenburg* made many turns and went over a storm during its final flight, encountered thunderstorms and rain in the last few hours. No cables broke during that stressful part of the voyage. Ok so let me get this straight. Just magically, a single cable above cell 2 on the starboard side snapped (but with no sound to be heard by the four crew members nearby) because it had not been "properly maintained" with enough energy (sparking somehow) to ignite the mysterious puff of hydrogen from somewhere out of a gas cell, finding just the right amount of air so it would ignite and burn *slowly* enough to provide the kindling for the resulting fire.

What a bunch of malarkey.

* * *

The New York Times on May 18, 12 days after the disaster, quotes the investigative board, "That they established definitely that the fire that destroyed the dirigible Hindenburg on May 6 was a hydrogen fire, but were unable to learn how the hydrogen was ignited."

Both investigating groups concluded that the ignition source was from an atmospheric electrical disturbance such as a brush discharge. The German commission favored the theory that the discharge was caused by equalization of tension (static) between wet spots on the exterior and the ship's framework. Neither investigative report documents any conclusion as to the origin of the presumed hydrogen–air mixture.

From Captain Lehmann, "To ignite or explode the hydrogen in the ship from other than premeditated or deliberate causes, would require escaping hydrogen or a free mixture of hydrogen and air, and a spark or flame as the igniting agency. But as the world knows, definite evidence to pin the cause of the fire conclusively on any of these agencies was lacking nor could it be shown that there was free hydrogen or any dangerous mixture of hydrogen and air present."

From Stacey, author of *The Hindenburg* (1990), " It was the Third Reich's policy, however, to never admit to any weakness. The idea of saboteurs bringing down the mighty Hindenburg was not acceptable to the German government, nor was the idea that a flaw in the design of the airship, or even simple human error, could have been responsible. Therefore, Hitler declared the disaster, 'an act of God.'"

From Commander Rosendahl, quoting Dr. Eckener, "As matters stand, there is not one possibility, but two, which might be interconnected. I would like to—because these possibilities are remote possibilities—I would be inclined to say that the possibility which I am about to state is an unlikely coincidence, because if it is necessary to assume two remote possibilities occurring at the same time, then the probability that these two remote possibilities concur is unlikely. But still, since the whole occurrence is extremely mysterious, we must proceed along these lines as the only sure point to start."

Rosendahl then states, "The theory involving the coincidence of two remote possibilities advanced by Doctor Eckener is practically the same as the conclusion reached by the official board of investigation."

A conclusion, which the Board admitted as being inconclusive.

What we know now is that there were 97 people on board the *Hindenburg*. Not one of them was a saboteur.

There were 97 witnesses at the Board of Inquiry. 97 people who testified to what they saw, heard, smelled and thought. No bomb or evidence of one was ever found. No gunshot was heard; no gun, bullet, nor evidence of such an event. No positive evidence was ever found pointing to leaking hydrogen.

* * *

I pause to recall that on Mom's 20th Christmas she was given a new radio. Dad recalled hearing of the *Hindenburg* disaster on it in 1937. All he could remember was something about hydrogen and the end of dirigibles. That 1931 Colin B Kennedy radio sits above on my computer desk, along with a picture of my mom with the radio next to it. I turn it on once in awhile to listen to music. Next to it is a flower vase that once sat on an aluminum dining table in the *Hindenburg* just before the disaster. It has a chip and a burn mark on it, attesting to "its" experience.

Chapter 8

Suspicions Aroused

"The cause of the 'Hindenburg' catastrophe was no mystery say LZ engineers: the coat of varnish was the problem," in: Schwabische Zeitung of 10.4.91.

In May of 1994 I took advantage of NASA's "buyout" program and retired after 32 years of federal service. I was sort of still in a state of shock that I would actually retire. I knew now with my Ph.D program that I was on my own without the anticipated NASA aid. My *Hindenburg* study was looking more like a strung out literary search with no justification of my idea (the cause of the disaster) even close. I was also reeling in depression over the fact that the university thought I was on a "fishing expedition." I poured over almost 40 years of my accumulated hydrogen documentation, planning a hydrogen based dissertation as a backup.

There was no question I would follow the hydrogen movement and continue to support the national and international conferences as well as continue as a member of the Department of Energy's Hydrogen Technical Advisory Panel. Also, I planned to continue with the ISO work on international standards for hydrogen technologies and codes and standards with the National Hydrogen Association in

Washington, D.C. I expected that travels associated with these events would provide me more opportunities to gather information regarding the research.

In June of 1994 the 10th World Hydrogen Energy Conference was taking place in Cocoa Beach, Florida. I was wandering around the audience when I spotted a guy with an airship book under his arm.

I said, "Excuse me but may I see that book for a second?" I wanted to check to see if I had a copy, as I did not recognize the cover. Sure enough it was a new book I had not seen.

"Is it for sale?" I asked. The guy said sure, twenty-five bucks. He took twenty.

Then he said, "Do you know Addison Bain, I'm looking for him to talk about hydrogen."

I said, "You're looking at him!"

It turns out the guy was Richard VanTreuren an airship historian and author. We had lunch and hit it off.

I told Richard about my idea of the *Hindenburg* envelope coating theory. It turns out he worked at the space center and worked on the Space Shuttle Orbiters and was quite familiar with solid rocket boosters.

He said, "Wow! Are you telling me the Hindenburg may have been coated with rocket fuel?"

I said, "Well, similar." I explained that the literature was not specific and the Board of Inquiry did not fully address the airship envelope coating.

Richard knew many airship authors, historians, artifact collectors and people who had worked at Lakehurst. He was tall, had a receding hairline, and sported a black beard. He could rattle off stuff about airships 'till you turned blue. I am sure he was well respected among the "helium heads" (airship people) with his vast airship knowledge. He invited Hepburn

Richard and Hep

Walker and me to his house so I could talk with "Hep" about what I was working on.

Hep had worked at Lakehurst in the early 1940's. One day he was sort of digging around the grounds at the airfield and came across some pieces of fabric and other items that were remnants of the disaster. He had saved these over the years.

"FABRIC?" I exclaimed. Needless to say at our next meeting Hep brought his artifacts.

"Aw, Hep, what's the chances of me borrowing one of those pieces?"

He said, "Okay as long as they were kept intact."

He was very cautious of my research and skeptical at first. I believe he became more excited later as events started to unfold. He knew a lot about airships and had studied details about them. Hep was very meticulous when discussing details, all the while looking at you with piercing eyes.

I knew NASA had a program of supporting public technical evaluation requests depending on the nature of the request and so long as the support did not upset the routine space program related work. For example, the local police had brought in a video clip from a bank surveillance camera that recorded a robbery. The lab was able to enhance one of the images to the point of determining the vehicle license plate number of the fleeing robbers. I also was very familiar with the capabilities of the labs, as I had had a lot of investigative work done on propellant and life support equipment problems over the years. Needless to say, I knew most of the people that worked in the labs and was familiar with the various disciplines of their expertise.

My first meeting with the investigators was to ask them to look at the artifacts and determine what analytical techniques could be employed without destroying the specimens. As it turned out many nondestructive techniques were available. However, to do a thorough job, a very small specimen would be needed. I was amazed, sort of, that all they needed was small piece about an eighth of an inch wide. NASA needed a protocol (step-by-step procedures) to be set up so that the specimen went through the lab in an orderly fashion. A frantic call was made to Hep to let him know the procedure. I assured him that the lab would consume only a small part of his artifact for some of the testing.

He said, "Go for it."

Then Richard put me in touch with Cheryl Ganz in Chicago. She headed up the Zeppelin Collectors Club and monitored their collection of airship artifacts. She had planned on coming to Tampa, Florida for a stamp collector's show. Sharon and I made arrangements to meet her there.

She brought with her not only artifacts from the

Hindenburg, but the *Graf Zeppelin* and LZ 130. Wow! The "Graf" was the airship built before the Hindenburg and LZ 130 was the airship built *after* the *Hindenburg.* This was a pivotal moment in my research. I could now compare the "changes" made, if any, in the doping material. Cheryl had a number of swatches of coated fabric from each of the three airships. It was fantastic!

Cheryl was rightly concerned over the welfare of her articles if I were to borrow them. After all, this was our first meeting. I was essentially a total stranger to her. She was a nice looking young lady, obviously very knowledgeable about the airship community. As she handed over items for me to borrow she reached over and touched my wife's arm.

"How do you feel about your first born?" she said. We got the message.

Cheryl Ganz

Off to the labs I went. My project was permeating throughout the lab at NASA and was coined the "H" project. It was touching the lives of fourteen individuals, expert in various fields such as electron microscopic analysis, spectrographic analysis, static electricity, photogrammetry, fire sciences and other material science disciplines using state of the art machines.

The Airship Heritage Foundation in England heard of the investigation. Via Richard, a representative envelope sample of the British airship, the R 101, was available as well. As you may recall, the R 101 was a large rigid airship that crashed and burned in France in October, 1930 killing all but three. Like the *Hindenburg*, that incident was never solved either, other than it crashed into a hill and burned. However that accident prompted the Germans to make major changes from the *Graf Zeppelin* to the *Hindenburg* design. I secured some R 101 fabric from Airship Heritage Foundation and handed it over to the NASA lab. The lab results revealed that the R 101 airship outer envelope coatings consisted of iron oxide and a pigmented aluminum particle cellulose nitrate substrate. The accident occurred in an electrically active thunderstorm. I leave it to the reader to come back to this, after reading this book, and ponder as to what the probable cause may have been.

The lab worked on the project over a span of about sixteen months. The reason it took so long was because there was a lot of priority work on space program projects going on. For me, the delay was a little grueling as I was getting only a little information at a time. The upside was that each finding was spectacular as the "case" unfolded. What the Zeppelin Company did and did not do was becoming very clear.

Each little piece of lab work was bringing the overall puzzle together. "But why is this information not in the literature?" I was asking myself. I mean, after over 9,000 references so far, I found nothing that would support the fact that a cellulose acetate butyrate compound (found by the lab) was not mentioned. Why did the investigative board not test the coated fabric to find, as the lab did, that it was not only highly flammable but was very resistive to conduct static electricity? After all, the outside of the airship (envelope) would build up a tremendous charge as it traveled through the atmosphere in addition to the influential conditions of electrical storms that fateful night at Lakehurst. And to make matters worse, what about the intimate mix of the first coat, iron oxide, and the successive coats of the aluminum powder-impregnated doping? We found bleed-through of the first aluminum coat with the

Thermite hot spots

iron oxide. The little spots of aluminum and iron oxide mix (shown in the photo), I coined as "Thermite hot spots."

I spent hours pouring over the reference material I had accumulated looking for anything that would tell me exactly what paint formulation was used to coat the *Hindenburg*. Nothing. I became more suspicious. With so much other information available, why wasn't the paint formula? All that was said during the Board of Inquiry was Chief Engineer Dr. Ludwig Duerr testifying, "By doping the outer cover, the inflammability became less, and we are using therefore Cellon and not the dope on a cellulose base." I was looking for a correlation between what the labs were coming up with and original airship design information. I did eventually come across a formulation used for "aluminum pigmented dope" in a technical report of the late 1920's. The information appeared very close to the analysis of envelope artifacts.

* * *

At a luncheon at a National Hydrogen Association Conference, I gave a ten- minute briefing about my efforts, and proposed that maybe hydrogen was not to blame for the initiation of the disaster but perhaps the highly flammable, or maybe even highly reactive nature of the chemicals used in the dopant was. I proposed they were the *Hindenburg's* Achilles' heel. Some participants thought I was on to something and some pooh-poohed my idea. The incentive to keep on with the work was inspired by several members of the Association later, in one-on-one discussions.

The need to study more about airships, the nature of large fires (especially those that were cellulose based as in forest fires), the behavior of electrostatic activity and lightning, and to go back through my personal library on hydrogen were clearly the next steps. Little did I know that what lay ahead was going to augment my research and get me thrust into the public eye where I would have to defend my work.

* * *

First, I needed to understand the *Hindenburg* fire. To do that, I first needed to understand forest fires. Then I had to attempt to mix in the data of the various chemicals and chemical compounds on board to discover the significance of their contribution to the disaster.

Every year we read about the devastation that forest fires cause. Even in moderate wind conditions these fires seem to run out of control in a matter of minutes. But in consideration of what the forest is "constructed" of, no wonder. The trees and brush are made up of wood and wood-like plant fibers. Some of the constituents of wildland "fuels" consist of resins, waxes, and oils having relatively high heating values.

So what is the point of all this? Wood consists of a high percentage of cellulose molecules. Over 90 percent of cotton fibers are cellulose, and 100 percent cotton was a common material to make envelope fabrics for airships, which was then coated with chemicals.

Another point of discussing forest fires is to note their behavior.

In the forest setting, fires can move along its canopy, or top of the trees, in what is known as a crown fire. A variation of the crown fire is a type called the plume-dominated fire.

Plume-dominated fires are associated with relatively low wind speeds, usually less than 20 miles per hour. They can cause unexpected and serious problems in at least two different ways. The first results when the size and intensity of the fire produces extreme turbulence at the base of a convection column that is self created. The resulting pulsing and turbulence increases fire intensity and heat transfer to adjacent fuel and hence accelerates fire spread. The process feeds on itself and accelerates as the convection column grows.

The second way in which a plume-dominated fire can be extremely dangerous occurs when a downburst of cold air descends from the convection column and blows outward along the surface at high speeds in all directions. These localized yet small winds can be extremely strong and very dangerous because of their sudden occurrence. If the small winds encounter the fire, which is very likely, the fire becomes wind-driven for a short but very violent period in which extreme spread rates can occur. A so-called downburst can happen and is initiated by evaporative cooling of any precipitation that may be in the area (a very humid day).

Last but not least is to understand about the intense heat and fire associated with these cellulose-based fires. You probably recall seeing the very bright whitish-yellow, orange, and reddish flames rapidly consuming trees and brush in the TV coverage or photos about forest fires. These very colorful fires are giving off radiation and therefore heat for a great distance. The colors come from the various chemicals and elements that make up the forest materials. For example, sodium will give off a yellow color. Just like in fireworks where strontium burns red, barium green, iron oxide orange and potassium and aluminum burns white. Traces of such elements provide the same colorization in forest fires.

Another important aspect of forest fires that has bearing on the *Hindenburg* accident is when the fire moves along the surface or crown driven even by a small wind, either by nature or one that is self created. This action will heat up the "fuel" of the treetops as it moves along. What this does is make the wood materials easier to ignite when the fire does reach that point and helps to speed up the flame front. So this makes matters worse, and of course makes the task of fighting fires more difficult than it already is.

Consider the miles of wood dowels and wood fairing strips used in the make up of the airship envelope. These wood segments provided support between the panels as well as protection to prevent the fabric from rubbing on the metal frame. The fairing strips were glued in place using an adhesive. Ramie cord, a type of hemp rope from Asia, (also cellulose), was used to tie the panels to the frame.

LZ-129
CROSS SECTION AT APEX
LONGITUDINAL NO. 18

"A"

WOODEN DOWEL SPACER

DURALUMIN
RIVETED SECTIONS W/
ALKYD/ACRYLIC
COATING W/
PHTHALOCYNANINE
DYE

"B"

"B"

GAS CELL

G/L
COTTON CLOTH (FABRIC TYP)
CELLOPHANE FILM
COTTON CLOTH

G/L: 1 COAT LATEX
#2-17 COATS GRADUATED
MIX, 100% GELATIN CENTER
LAST COAT LATEX

RAMIE CORD
NETTING TO
CONTROL SHAPE &
POSITION ~ 30 CM. SPC'G
WIRE MESH TO TRANSMIT
LOADS TO FRAMING
~ 60 CM. SPACING

SECTION B-B

FINE WEAVE, COTTON, SEAM
COVER FLAP (AL DOPE ONLY)

RAMIE CORD
(S.E. ASIA HEMP)

WOODEN
FAIRING STRIP
(ADHESIVE)

STICHING

2 PIECE, COURSE
WEAVE CLOTH

FINE WEAVE
COTTON

LACING
THROUGH HOLES
IN ALUM. CHANNEL)

120-130 GM/M² COTTON
ENVELOPE PANEL W/
1 COAT IRON OXIDE
4 COATS CELLON W/ AL
POWDER (3%)

BRASS EYELET

(FIG. EXPANDED TO SHOW DETAIL)

DETAIL "A"

A. BAIN 1996

Almost seventeen acres of fabric was used to cover the airship. The fabric was cotton, a fabric that is 90 percent cellulose, soaked with dopant resins. The gas cells were made with cloth, cellophane and had a ramie cord netting around them. The walls of the cabins, dining room and other rooms were painted fabric materials.

The cellulose of the fabrics and the cellulose of the dowels, fairing strips and cords were the "forest" fuel that fed the fire making it hotter and hotter.

Fires are unpredictable. Many factors influence their behavior. For example, visualize trying to light a newspaper with a match. If a match is lit on top of a tightly rolled-up newspaper, little more than scorching can be expected. If the same newspaper is crumpled into a puffy column and the same match is lit under an exposed edge at the bottom, the paper is history. In both cases, the ignition temperature, the fuel, the available oxygen, and the ignition source is the same, but the result is dramatically different. Fires are very complex depending on the variety of fuels available and environmental conditions at the time.

Now you are prepared to better understand what was being witnessed at that inferno that took place at the Lakehurst Naval Air Station in the late afternoon of May 6, 1937.

* * *

We talked about fuel in the forest and we know a lot of forest fires are caused from lightning—a common ignition source. So next lets take a look at environmental conditions.

"Tongues of fire are licking around the muzzles of my machine-guns, and around my head too. And when I spread my hand, little flames spurt out of my fingertips." The man is describing an experience aboard the Zeppelin airship LZ 98.

The name, St. Elmo's fire, is attached to this very common phenomenon. Recorded in such historical books as "Moby Dick" and "Hakluyt's Voyages," sea-going men first observed this atmospheric electrical activity aboard their boats especially in the "crows nest" near the top of the mast. The name St. Elmo is from a modification of St. Erasmus, the patron saint of sailors of the Mediterranean.

Airships in flight acquire an electrostatic charge due to impact of dust and moisture particles in the atmosphere. This effect is noticeable at 40 kilometers per hour, increasing approximately as the 16th power of the airship speed. What this means is that the stuff will accumulate on the ship pretty fast. Electrostatic charges can also be induced on an airship from its motion near cloud formations. In fact, the large airships actually behave like clouds in the build up of electrical charges. The way electrical charges build up in clouds is best explained by the science museum near my house. The museum has a display of an electrostatic generator demonstrating how cloud-to-ground lightning works. The ground potential becomes positive as the wind currents strip and carry the electrons from the ground to the bottom of the cloud. The top of the cloud becomes positive, but the build up of the electrons causes enough voltage potential relative to the ground to cause the clouds to "relieve" themselves by an electron discharge to the ground. This is the visible part of the lightning stroke.

Studies by German electrostatic expert, Professor Max Dieckmann, in the 1920's, show that airships could acquire a significant level of electrostatic charge as influenced by nearby cloud formations through the process of induction. Walking across a carpeted floor and touching a doorknob will illustrate the charge of an electrostatic induction process. One of his papers shows induced voltages on a "medium" sized airship as

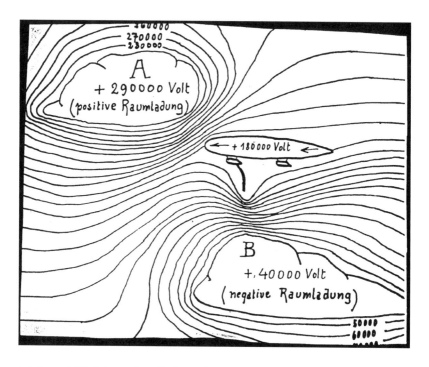

high as 180,000 volts. Other observations noted were the engine exhaust particles taking on a negative electrical charge because the engines were at the bottom of the airship – just like clouds, negative on the bottom.

More than a century after Benjamin Franklin used a kite to demonstrate the electrical nature of lightning, *Popular Science* recreated the experiments using sophisticated electrometers. Among the findings: thunderstorms were not the only condition yielding marked electrical effects, sparks were obtained in cloudless skies. Also, voltages increased as the kite rose. In a 1917 Royal Aeronautical Society report, it is stated, "The mean atmospheric voltage gradient with height is, in fine weather, 300 volts per meter, and in thundery conditions may be many times that amount."

A report by the National Academy for Civil Aeronautics, released in July 1924, cautions: "Airship envelope materials should offer no resistance to the passage of electric current or act as a dielectric (nonconductive). In order to prevent the airship from becoming too highly charged with electricity, it is desirable for all conducting masses to have projecting points in considerable number throughout the entire length of the airship, except in the vicinity of valves or where gas can escape."

The German airship *Bodensee* was actually struck by a direct flash of lightning that caused considerable fusion of the metal near the points of entry and exit of discharge. The metal framework of the hull was, however, of sufficient cross-sectional area to take the current without excessive heat, except near the points of entry and exit.

During my investigation at the materials science lab at KSC, we subjected a piece of the *Hindenburg* fabric to a low voltage (30 K) electrical discharge. What was interesting was at a perpendicular arrangement, the arc simply went through the fabric and nothing happened. The arc seemed to follow through the "hole" it produced as the path of least resistance. There wasn't enough contact time to build up heat on the fabric. An example of a lightning strike was being observed. However, allowing the arc to flow across the fabric in a parallel fashion caused immediate ignition. The phenomena made me consider the electron flow within the fabric with serious interest.

Electron flow in the atmosphere is of serious interest too, even though the various forms of atmospheric electrical activity are still a matter of debate. An attempt was made to characterize them into five categories: ball lightning, corona discharge, point discharge, space discharge and spark discharge. Even today scientists are uncovering new types of "flashes" such as sprites and blue jets that appear connected to thunderstorms but typically occur in the upper atmosphere.

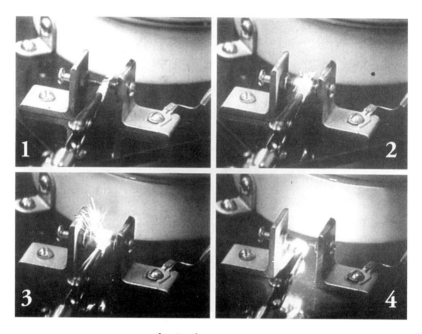

Arc testing sequence

During my research, I attempted to gather information from airline pilots about their experiences with electrical discharges on or around the aircraft in flight, especially near storm clouds. Some pilots were willing to tell me, but others preferred not to disclose their experiences, especially commercial airline guys, uncomfortable about how I was going to use the information. One retired pilot experienced a glow appearing around the cockpit window frame that manifested itself into a ball, entered the cockpit and "danced" along the floor to the rear of the aircraft. Another account with two witnesses, described an event that occurred during no thunderstorm activity but under cloudy conditions where a ball, blue-green in color, bounced on top of the wing leaving a black scuffed appearance.

A report from a well-known commercial airline, documents the accounts of numerous pilots with "many thousands of hours of flying experience" near and around lightning. They almost unanimously agree that there are two distinct types of activity. One is while flying in precipitation near freezing conditions, a corona is observed for several seconds then discharges. The second variety occurs abruptly with no warning. It is most likely near thunderstorms. Pilots believe there is a slow buildup type of charge from flying through the precipitation. A brilliant flash and a boom can be heard throughout the airplane.

I have talked with Navy guys who have served on the flight deck of an aircraft carrier. They have witnessed that when an approaching aircraft comes in, there is usually a noticeable spark discharge from the rear-landing wheel to the deck of the ship just before touch down.

The US Air Force Research Lab at Wright Patterson Air Force Base in Ohio became interested in my *Hindenburg* study. Electrical engineers indicated that all aircraft (including airships) would pick up what they call "p-static," or precipitation static buildup just flying through the air. The intensity increases as the surrounding atmosphere becomes more electrified by say, thunderstorm activity. Next time you fly on a commercial airplane, notice that out near the tip of the wings on the trailing edge there are a number of short protruding cables. These are carbon-impregnated wicks designed to discharge electrostatic buildup to keep you safe and comfy.

The science of electrostatics has been around for some time, but the relatively new science of electrostatic discharge or ESD has become important. The presence of electrostatic charge creates problems in many industries. The ESD potential damage in fields of electronic, photographic and medical applications could be significant. While electrostatic charges cannot be eliminated, they can be controlled. In the handling of rocket solid propellant segments or explosive devices, ESD is cause for concern for obvious reasons. I had the good fortune of being a keynote speaker at the 22nd ESD Association Symposium in September of 2000, presenting my *Hindenburg* research. During the symposium the Association permitted me to sit in on many tutorials devoted to a variety of ESD theory and applications. I learned a lot.

* * *

The 11th World Hydrogen Energy Conference was in Stuttgart, Germany in late June of 1996. I was aware that there was going to be some Zeppelin airship events the first part of July that year in Friedrichshafen (where the *Hindenburg* was built), a train ride from Stuttgart. They were celebrating the 96th flight of the first Zeppelin as well as the opening of the new museum. I also learned that there was a full-scale reconstruction of a 130-foot long section of the legendary LZ –129.

Serendipitously, the Zeppelin Company under a NASA contract, made, of all things, the dome sections of the Space Shuttle's liquid *hydrogen* fuel tanks! Ah ha! I thought, a way in to see the plant and discuss my research with the Zeppelin experts. So early 1996, I started communicating with the Zeppelin Company and by July had a formal invitation. I was also aware of a new museum in Friedrichshafen in which, as I understood it, had "some" LZ airship information. Historians I knew cautioned me not to be surprised if I didn't get to see much at the museum archive. The word was that Hitler (maybe Goering) ordered all reports, drawings and so forth of the airships be destroyed. Also, I was cautioned not to expect much cooperation from the museum.

Friedrichshafen is a very picturesque village next to the Bodensee (Lake Constance). One can see the gorgeous mountains of Austria and Switzerland across the lake. I could not communicate in German, but I had absolutely no trouble with the people. They were all so friendly and cooperative. The next morning the secretary of the engineering department picked me up from Hotel Hansa and took me to the Zeppelin plant. I was given a tour of the plant by the head of the department and got my picture taken next to the forming rig used to stamp out the Shuttle fuel tank domes. During lunch I discussed my research. I raised the question about what might be in the plant archives on the *Hindenburg*. I was told what ever is available is now down at the museum. So off we went.

On the way, we stopped to see the new Zeppelin under construction called the NT, for "New Technology." It was basically complete except for the outer envelope. I sat in one of the passenger seats and marveled at the luxury, nothing like an airline, not even first class. I also was allowed to sit in the pilot seat and was given a "cockpit tour."

The museum laid out the red carpet to say the least. The LZ manager of engineering introduced me to the museum archivian, Barbara. The people went out of their way to see that I could review what ever they had, reports, books, and drawings.

"Drawings? You have design drawings of the Hindenburg?" I asked.

"Yes and the Graf Zeppelins I and II (LZ 127 and LZ 130)", was Barbara's reply.

"Which parts (topics) of the airships would you like to look at?" she asked.

It took me awhile to catch my breath. I spent every

available minute in the museum skipping lunch or whatever, as time was now a premium for three days. I knew I would need to return.

Barbara was so helpful in getting through the indexes that were in German. With her help I managed to look for key words in German so that I could spot information that was on file. She was a very pretty petite brunette and was relatively new at her job. She was very familiar with what the museum had and was extremely helpful. After selecting the file numbers of interest, they were brought up from the basement for my review. It was clear many files had not been opened for some time. The slight whiff of fine dust finally got to me. I had a head cold by flight time back to the US.

Using a language cross reference I managed to identify what appeared to be very interesting titles. I was able to copy those of interest knowing I could get translation help back in the United States. One stood out clearly in German after a little self-translation. "Report of fabric fire testing – LZ 129." Wow! A gold mine, and it did not quit! Why was all this kept secret though, I wondered? And what else is there still "hidden" in the files. I was frustrated that I had not continued with my German classes in college.

As I went through the airship drawings, I noticed that the LZ -129 drawings were used for LZ -130. Where appropriate, each drawing sheet had a stamp placed on it indicating,

"Approved for LZ-130." However the LZ-130 file did have some sheets depicting what at first appeared as innocuous, or subtle, changes. As a former draftsman I was used to the practice of identifying changes in a "revision" block near the signature block. Yes there they were—the <u>Anderung</u> or list of changes. But on drawing H1720 of the <u>Umbullung</u> or hull drawing, some changes were noted on the passenger area and the motor gondola area. I made a copy in that there were tables of the

<u>Anstrichfolge</u>: 1x mit rot (Eisenoxyd) 2%, Eck 10÷18
1x farblos, Eck 0÷10 St.Bu.B.B.
4x mit Alumin.-Bronce 2% Eck 0÷18

Änderung: Motorengondel, Hüllenspieren, verstärkte Leinenhülle
10.Ⅲ.38. Rw.
Änderung: Fahrgastraum-Ausbau 16.12.37. Rw.
Änderung vom 20.Ⅳ.37. Rw.; 30.Ⅳ.37 Rw. Stückl. 130 Hd.

<u>Umhüllung.</u> LZ.130

H1720

Courtesy Zeppelin Archives

weights of fabric used and some coating data, which I thought might be useful to me.

It was not until I got back to the US that I took more time to read through the drawings and painstakingly translated stuff with my handy dandy "Cassell's German-English Dictionary."

Lets see, <u>Anstrichfolge</u>. Ok, "coat of paint sequence." Great! Just what I was looking for. I read on. First coat, <u>Eisenoxyd</u> – the typical iron oxide first coat on <u>Eck 10 – 18</u>, or the top part of the airship. Okay, same as the LZ-129. Then, <u>4 x mit Alumin-Bronce</u> <u>2% Eck 0 – 18</u> stood out.

I'll be damned! They switched from the 3% pure aluminum powder as used on the LZ-129 to a 2% aluminum bronze. The bronze would be heavier, so going from 3% to 2%, I rationalized, would compensate for its weight, which is something one wants to reduce. But bronze, aluminum bronze, has a high percentage of copper, just the thing to reduce flammability and increase conductivity of the outer cover.

Fantastic! Another goldmine. Here it was just nonchalantly changed. A significant change at that!

Now my suspicions grew deeper.

Back at home one night, I woke up like a shot to realize, "Wait! The lab did not find any copper on the LZ-130 fabric sample I had. They found the typical dopant but with calcium sulfamate added."

I contacted my source of the specimen to get a reading where the fabric came from, and was it really the LZ-130. For several days sitting on pins and needles I finally got a call to say, "I can tell you the person that acquired it says it came from the engine gondola, not the hull, but I can not reveal the name of the person or they will get into trouble."

That's it, they used the calcium sulfamate, a fire retardant used in the textile industry, on the engine gondola fabric covering. That made sense. Engine fuel or oil could spill or leak onto the covering rendering it more flammable, so it would require more protection. The lab finding was no longer a mystery.

A colleague of mine found correspondence in the Karl Arnstein collection at the University of Akron Archives concerning the pigment change. One document dated November 22nd and the other the 23rd, 1938, discussed the change. "The aluminum powder to Luftschiffbau Zeppelin. This material is what is known commercially by the Aluminum Co. of America as 'aluminum bronze powder, Alcoa #422, extra fine.' 100% of the powder will go through a 325-mesh screen."

On my third visit to Germany and the Zeppelin Archives, I finally found much correspondence on the airship coating process. Most of the letters were dated in July 1937. They indicated the use of cellulose acetate on LZ-127 and a "butter-acid" for the LZ-129. It was suggested that for LZ-130 that the dopant be sprayed on rather than the mop-and-bucket approach as used on LZ-129. A smooth and uniform coating would be achieved.

"Painting" the airship.

As I mentioned before, up until the LZ-130, the engines were the pusher type. That means the propeller was in the rear of the engine car. After many tests the Zeppelin Company chose to modify the design using the tractor or pull configuration with the prop in front. This was a major and costly change, or so it has been written. The reason behind the change is because it adapted very well to incorporate a water recovery system, which also changed the engine exhaust system. I have only found two airship people that were suspicious about the change. The change would reduce the typical exhaust plume (hot sparks on occasion) over the aft portion of the airship. This was clearly another safety consideration over the LZ-129 design.

From writer Laurie Soffe, "While the arrangement was stated to have aerodynamic advantages, it may have also been influenced by electrical factors. The propellers, particularly in dry air, generated an ionized slipstream. Since at that time the cause of the Hindenburg loss was still being investigated, placing the propellers ahead of substantial metallic structures, namely the engine cars, could help in absorbing some of this ionization, allowing it to be harmlessly dispersed into the airship's framework. Thus any charge carried towards the craft's fins by the slipstream would be minimized; as the LZ-129 fire started in the stern area it would be a logically prudent arrangement."

Before the museum officially opened, I took a break and had the opportunity to go inside where the full-scale mock-up of the *Hindenburg* was.  It was an authentically furnished passenger and staff lounge. You could stand at the windows, look out, and daydream about what the real flights must have been like. Airship travel had to be one of the most enjoyable ways to travel in the sense you were really "traveling" and not being whisked from one location to another.

As part of the festivities in Friedrichshafen, there were art shows, exhibits and an airship collector's show. I met a collector from Berlin who had a number of airship items. He tried to sell me a dinner plate from the *Hindenburg*, so he claimed. I pointed to some fabric pieces and examined them.

"Shop samples they call these," he said.

He claimed they were from the shop during construction of the airship. They looked, smelled and felt authentic or at least a good replica. I thought to myself, "I don't have any specimens with the iron oxide coating on the backside like these. I could do a correlation study." This meant comparing the data taken from the various lab machines of the specimens known to be authentic, and doing the same analysis of the shop samples. If that turned out okay then these would make excellent specimens for the destructive testing such as the arc tests. They could also be used in the flame hood for flammability measurements. I purchased what he had, but it meant money would be tight for the rest of the trip. I was spending unplanned funds at the archive as it was.

I could not get back to the states soon enough to get the translation going. It turned out to be more difficult than I realized. Some reports were in "old German" and were hand written. NASA came to the rescue. With space payloads built by other countries intended to fly on vehicles at the Cape, I knew NASA had to have access to private translators. I found one that could read what I had, even the "old German" stuff. Great, but it took time and a few coins to get done.

Of first priority was to perform the flame testing. At first I went to NASA for initial testing. I then went to the Fire Science Laboratory at the Florida Institute of Technology (FIT) to perform more extended study. The conclusion was that once the fabric was burning the flame was self-sustaining. At FIT we went a step further to show the "Thermite hot spot" reaction. As the specimen burned, just touching it with a metal rod,

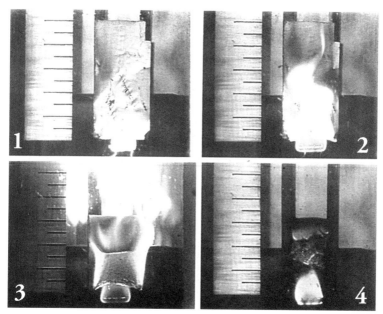

Flame tests

droplets of Thermite were produced and they bounced on the lab bench. The testing was video recorded by Pangolin Pictures for National Geographic Television. The recording was for the documentary, *Hindenburg: Titanic Of The Air.*

I am devoted to Ben Jordan for his effort to come up with an electrical arc machine in which I used to show how the

Thermite demonstration

Hindenburg fabric would easily ignite by an electrical discharge. This was done at Frank Lynch's facility in Denver. I used a piece of the original fabric (thanks to Jay Ciser of Palm Coast, Florida) for this experiment.

I visited the museum in Friedrichshafen again, sponsored by Pangolin Pictures, and had the same opportunity to get additional information. On my last visit I was no longer allowed to make photocopies of the drawings. Not that the secrets were getting out, but copier light over time would fade the delicate drawings. I understood. So laboriously, I took a lot of notes, even in German when I stumbled a little. I found even more reports of interest. The most impressive report had to do with electrical arc testing of the LZ-129 fabric. They found it was easy to ignite. The report concluded that the *doped fabric was the flaw contributing to the disaster*!

I sat in amazement. Why me? Why was I to find this?

To my surprise I found several interesting reports that I was allowed to copy and have translated. The reports were German investigations done later in 1937. Of note were three principal studies:

1. Dr. Max Dieckmann, Munich Technical Institute, conducted comparative tests of the LZ-127 envelope and LZ-129 envelope to find the latter to be nonconductive and prone to static electricity build up. He also used models to simulate what would happen. In the case of the *Graf Zeppelin* makeup nothing happened, but the *Hindenburg* makeup, "got a fire" the report stated. Dieckmann also predicted that the electrical potential on the *Hindenburg* at the time of landing could have been as high as 100,000 volts. (Mrs. Dieckmann later wrote a letter to me about her husband's tests. At the time, he could not publish all the data. The reasons being she said, were for possible

insurance claims and the other reason was not to embarrass the Third Reich).

2. Testing by the Wireless Telegraph and Atmospheric Electrical Station reports said, "The basic cause of the catastrophic fire is ultimately to be regarded as the poor conductivity of the aluminum paint coating on the outer skin and the good insulation of the blue anti-corrosion paint of the framework. Also, If the landing tow ropes had been attached to the ship's hatches directly, then the total conductivity value of the tow lines probably could not have reached the required amount for discharge, or only then after the ship had been hauled down to a lower height, when the field strength would not have been sufficient." It is noted that the landing attempt was a "high landing" not a good practice for the *Hindenburg* in a highly electrified environment.

3. An electrical engineer in Germany, Otto Beyersdorf, running tests with the airship covering found that it was readily ignited by an electrostatic discharge. He goes on to report, "An incombustible gas cannot prevent a burning of the covering as long as this one has the characteristics of the test result." suggesting the disaster would have taken place even if helium had been used.

Then comes the icing on the cake.

Dr. S. R. Scaggs did much work at the Los Alamos National Laboratory on oxidation-reduction reaction experiments with iron oxide and aluminum flake (experiments which measure reduction of oxygen in the chemical mixture when an energy source is applied). He indicated in a letter to me that the reaction occurs on a very rapid time scale, typically microseconds depending on the mix intimacy. A bright orange light is associated with it. He says, "The 'lightning dazzles' on the surface of the Hindenburg seen by the witnesses, most likely created a temperature that was hot enough to initiate these reactions. The reaction would have proceeded over the surface of the envelope within just a few seconds." All it took was electron flow through the mixture. He sent me a report entitled, *The Thermochemistry of Selected Ballotechnic Reactions* for me to review the detail. All it did was add more fuel to the fire!

Aluminum powder used in the *Hindenburg* dopant is also used in explosives and fireworks. The bombing in Oklahoma City involved fertilizer (ammonium nitrate) and diesel fuel. However, terrorists must first add a compound such as aluminum powder to adjust the temperature threshold in which the compounds would explode in order for the detonator to effectively do its job.

The Space Shuttle solid rocket boosters use an oxidizer called ammonium perchlorate and a fuel called powdered aluminum. Iron oxide is also blended in to regulate the combustion process of the rocket propellant. Iron oxide, as you remember, was also found in the *Hindenburg's* paint.

Aluminum powder when mixed with iron oxide is the basis of Thermite, used to weld heavy sections of metal. The temperature of burning Thermite can reach 5,000 deg F. The reaction of aluminum powder sequestered in butyl acetate can reach 3,278 deg F according to the Air Force chemistry lab. The bottom part of the *Hindenburg* was coated with the aluminum and clear acetate. Iron oxide was added to the coating for the top of the airship.

The *Hindenburg's* aluminum frame was coated with an alkyd/acrylic lacquer containing a phthalocynanine dye. The purpose was to reduce corrosion as experienced on LZ –127. Unfortunately, the coating allowed the frame surface to be nonconductive, so tests showed. To make matters, worse the coating would burn.

I am indebted to Dr. Merrill for his work on the chemical kinetics of the *Hindenburg* doped envelope compounds. Using the Air Force Research Laboratory's proprietary computer program, he found that the combustion/decomposition temperature of the *Hindenburg* coating used on the top of the airship to be 3347 degrees F. He also shared with me the Air Force findings of the incompatibility of flake powdered aluminum and static electricity. This fact was not known until 1986, almost 50 years after the *Hindenburg* disaster. The information was discovered because a Pershing missile exploded killing workers loading up the missiles' solid propellant segments. The conclusion was that the flake-powdered aluminum used was very sensitive to electrostatic discharge. They found that the spherical configuration (now used today) of the imbedded aluminum particulate was less sensitive and therefore safer.

I went back to the lab to check on the *Hindenburg* fabric again because the flake feature had not been an issue up until now. Guess what? Yep, the flake configuration was used.

Merrill was also able to provide some enthalpy data (heats of formation). I now knew the heat flux, the rapid thermal conductivity of the hydrogen in cell 1, the extreme radiation of the carbon-based fire, the convection of heat across the cover to the cell air space, the rapid heat conductivity of the aluminum frame, and the status of cell fullness. It seemed to me the needed data was at hand to model what was happening. All cell 1 needed was a temperature rise of about 120 degrees F to reach fullness or almost the elastic limit of the gelatin/latex-cloth/cellophane membrane. The cell was constrained by a netting of ramie cord and steel wires meant to control the cell so it would not make contact with the aluminum frame just inches away. Concurrently, the aluminum frame would weaken with the rapid heat conduction typical for aluminum. I am trying to visually create the sequence of the bursting of the rear of the airship.

Courtesy Zeppelin Archives

First, it is important to understand the configuration of cell 1 and 2. When you see a picture of the airship, the very rear (stern) is cone shaped, extending beyond the fins. This is where cell 1 was. The cell did not have a relief valve (a device to release excess pressure). There was a "flow tunnel" less than one foot in diameter, about 12 feet *below* the cell centerline, interfacing with cell 2. The cell 1 forward bulkhead was about 50 feet in diameter. The cell held about 50,000 cubic feet of gas. Cell 2 did have a relief valve 12 feet *above* the centerline on its forward bulkhead at a distance of 50 feet from the "flow tunnel." The valve had a flow capacity of 164 cubic feet per second. Cell 2 had a volume

NASA Photo Lab

194

of 120,000 cubic feet. Therefore the single relief valve had to service both cells 1 and 2. Clearly to me, the relief valve wasn't adequate to handle any rapid expansion of gas. One of the first photos of the fire shows the absence of the rear cone—basically cell 1.

An attempt to develop a heat transfer model is complex. The variation of the doping process, trying to estimate the heat transformation from the fabric to the cells versus the heat loss to the surrounding environment make the modeling very tricky. Choosing the percent contribution of normal fabric burning, the fuel sequestered in the oxidizer mix reaction, and the Thermite reaction contribution, can only be arbitrary assumptions. However, I did do some back of the envelope calculations.

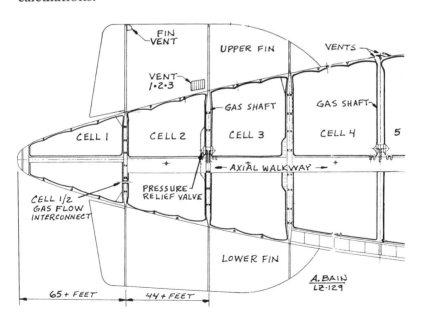

I did not consider the complicated ballotechnic based reactions and used the straightforward ΔQ (heat flux) approach. I chose a moment in time when one-tenth of the rear cone stern, (upper/starboard area) was burning. I assumed 85% of the heat energy was radiated to the outside air/environment. Now I don't know the bursting pressure of the cell, but if you buy seven pounds per square inch (which is 30 times the relief value setting in cell 2) there was still over two times the available heat energy needed to burst the cell. *Could this have been the "frump" helmsman Lau heard*, I wondered.

Heat transfer in hydrogen is very rapid. Simply put, there was a lot of energy created in a very short period of time before hydrogen as a fuel got into the act. Clearly the photos and sound recordings validate the sequence that took place. The expanding cell had to first overcome the elastic limit of its material, then the constraining netting. Next it had to overcome the containment of the frame, albeit it was rapidly weakening from the intense heat. Hydrogen is then released and mixed with air; some of it ignites (a fuel rich condition), adding to the fireball.

Suspicions aroused? What do you think?

* * *

I was under pressure to get my dissertation draft to the college for committee review. I had finished the required engineering management courses. Normally, five years is the time span given for the Ph.D. program and that was coming near. I got permission for an extension, but targeted October of 1998 as the drop-dead date to have the dissertation in final hard copy and my final exam completed. I had enough information to formulate the point of the research theory, and the committee concluded that as well. I needed to start preparing for my oral presentation, which wound up with 120 slides of all the principal facets of the investigation.

The final written exam had a number of time-consuming

questions to answer in essay form. The one that I struggled with was, "Give an example of a superior technology which is currently available to provide something of benefit to mankind but which is not implemented because of public fear, do not include hydrogen or nuclear topics." I picked Solar Power Satellites, a case for laser/power beam energy. After a couple of months in the library and on the Internet I was beginning to think my selection was going to result in a thesis in itself!

Finally, I was finished. As I picked up the copy from the printers, 160 pages, gold embossed printing on a dark blue cover, my teary eyes looked over to see my wife, teary eyed as well. She understood what it took to get to this point. As we drove back home she held the book in her lap looking down and could not stop saying, "Wow!" *The Hindenburg Disaster: A Compelling Theory of Probable Cause and Effect*, by Dr. Addison Bain, Ph.D.

By October, I was at the university giving my oral exam and presenting my hard copy dissertation. "Congratulations, Dr. Bain," are words I'll never forget as the university dean of engineering shook my hand. I went to an ocean side restaurant and had a basket of calamari and a couple of Coronas, without the lime. I sat and stared at the beautiful ocean, as my eyes filled with happy tears. Mom's dream had come true. My wife would be excited. As I knew she was sitting on pins and needles at home waiting for the phone call, but I had to wait a bit to control the emotion.

To say the least, I was exhausted, but relieved, as I am sure other people are when they complete their Ph.D. program, but the research was not over in my mind. There seemed to still be some loose ends. Even though many of my peers and fellow colleagues felt my work was an excellent example of professional forensic science, I was still troubled by some minute details. So I knew I would be doing some more digging. There were still a few critics of the work that had some good points to follow through with, and there were still a few "armchair experts" holding to the hydrogen theory. Little did they know the Zeppelin company engineers had already conceded to the doped fabric theory based on their own work. But I had not found any report that offered an explanation of why the fire seemed to start at the upper starboard aft quadrant, as the collective evidence suggests. So I needed to work on the "smoking gun."

* * *

The time was right again to see my folks in Kalispell. It was too late in the year to go to the Twins. Dad was now in a nursing home. When I visited him it was just after lunch and he was being pushed to his room in a wheelchair. I held my emotions, as this was not a sight I was prepared for. He immediately recognized me and held out his hand for a handshake. Dad never hugged anyone except Mom. In the room I showed him the "Blue Book." Dad ran his trembling hand over and over the gold embossed printing of the title on the cover. His eyes filled with tears telling me the "Dr." was a satisfying accomplishment. He thought only medical people were "doctors," his dream.

"Am sorry Add but I will not be able to read this," he said. I understood, but it was another emotional event now realizing he could no longer read because of his slowly degrading eyesight. I explained the project and handed him the piece of fabric from the airship discussing the features I had found. This 89-year-old ex-powder monkey, fondling the fabric, then said, "Well Add, they should have known better. I could have used this stuff to blow up the rock on the Going-To-The-Sun road project in Glacier Park." I told him I was still looking into his oxygen concern.

"Well good, but I am not worried anymore. They keep pestering me with that in this place."

Chapter 9

Exonerating Hydrogen

"The destruction of the airship LZ-129 Hindenburg, marked the end of airship travel."

This statement seems to appear in news articles every May 6, the annual anniversary of the infamous disaster. One would think the Zeppelinwerks closed their doors to airship construction. In other articles it is noted Zeppelinwerks went on to make aluminum fuel tanks for the V-2 rockets in the war against England. Actually, a few years went by before this latter event took place.

Nevertheless for the LZ-130, sister ship to the LZ-129, construction continued. Another airship, the LZ-131, was started and a larger airship, the LZ-132, was on the drawing board. All intentions of continuing with the vision of worldwide civil passenger service which persisted at the Zeppelinwerks was set back only momentarily. Like major aircraft disasters and like the Space Shuttle *Challenger* disaster, the engineers regroup, find the flaws and go on about building and flying a "better" machine.

Such was the case with the "new" airship.

Almost a full year before the Lakehurst event on the 23rd of June 1936, the keel of the LZ-130 had been laid along with some of the first frame rings. The framework of the airship was basically a braced framework of light metal girders consisting of rings, longitudinal girders and a load-bearing keel. The airship was divided into several bays by braced rings in which were located the sixteen gas cells. The framework and molding were covered with a fabric hull, outside of which the four engine gondolas are mounted. In addition to the keel, which also served as a walkway for the crew from one end of the airship to the other, was an axial walkway running through the center of the hull. Basically the design was a mirror image of the LZ-129.

The initial decision was made to go to 100% helium, which meant a reconstruction of LZ-130. By August 1937 the necessary changes were identified. These involved reducing the passenger area from seventy to forty passengers, adaptation of an engine exhaust water recovery system and a general lightening of the total assembly. Interesting to note, the engine exhaust gases contained a considerable amount of water. Thus, as fuel was used, the recovery of the water compensated for loss of weight (water used for ballast) and therefore the expensive helium would not have to be vented during normal operations.

The completion date was set for April,1938, and the first flight to the US was planned for the first week in May 1938, one year after the LZ-129 disaster.

During the completion of LZ-130, Dr. Eckener from the Zeppelin Company made numerous attempts to negotiate the purchase of helium from the only known source, the US. He ran into many roadblocks, even after conferring with President Roosevelt. During my research I found that US Secretary of the Interior, Harold Ickes, was most instrumental in rejecting Germany's request. Apparently Ickes was concerned Hitler might use the airship for military reasons, even though Dr.

Eckener appeared to convince Roosevelt that a Zeppelin would not be used for military purposes.

Giving up with the United States, the Zeppelinwerks made application to Germany's Air Transport Minister for permission to undertake experimental and test flights with the LZ-130, *using hydrogen.* On September 13, 1938, a flight license was granted to go ahead with the test flights prior to the acceptance of the LZ-130 for operational flights. During the test-flight period no fee-paying passengers would be aboard, and flying was limited to Germany near open water. On September 14, the hydrogen-filled airship lifted off on its inaugural flight, and in ten hours covered 575 miles.

It seems that as the number of flights increased the number of passengers increased. On flight No. 3, the crew and 19 technicians doing experimental work were on board. Equipment was loaded on board for the purpose of conducting research into the *Hindenburg* catastrophe where electrical discharges were judged to be the cause of the accident. On flight 14 there were 47 crewmembers and 10 "guests." Flight 17, 46 crew and 24 "people." Flight 16 had 33 "passengers."

With 43 crew members and 13 guests on board flight No. 30, the LZ-130 took part in the Flying Day at Essen-Mulheim with 200,000 spectators in attendance. From there it went to Frankfurt, and this flight was the last flight of any Zeppelin. The "restriction" to fly near open water was ignored at all times.

In command of LZ-130, starting with flight No. 5, was Albert Sammt, watch officer along with Heinrich Bauer, also watch officer on the fateful final flight of the *Hindenburg.* Captain Max Pruss with scars, having been badly burned from the *Hindenburg* fire, also flew on a number of flights. Mechanic Bentele (also on the *Hindenburg's* last flight) flew on flight number 3. There were no apparent reservations about flying with hydrogen.

Disappointment came when the Third Reich made the decision to dismantle the remaining airships to use the metal for war machines. So on the 1st of September, 1939, the LZ-130 emptied all of its almost seven million cubic feet of hydrogen into the atmosphere in preparation for dismantling. The same day, Hitler declared war on Poland and the Second World War began.

With war declared, the new ship joined the veteran *Graf Zeppelin*, LZ-127, and the Nazi government unceremoniously dismantled both. It was said that they had no military value and the material of the precious aluminum frames were needed to make rockets and planes. So Ickes was right, Hitler did use the Zeppelins for military purposes – just not in the way anyone imagined!

On May 6, 1940, the third anniversary of the *Hindenburg* catastrophe at Lakehurst, the hanger in Frankfurt, once used for the LZ-130 was demolished. It was said that the hangers built for the mighty airships were in the way of fighter planes taking off from the nearby runway.

Although all the plans for a passenger airship service had been completed, Germany's leadership had plans only for war, rather than for peace and understanding between peoples. As a result, the LZ-130 was fated to be the last of the great Zeppelins. Dr. Hugo Eckener and his company were disappointed.

The demise of LZ-130 did one other thing; it destroyed the evidence of engineering flaws of the LZ-129. Thanks to a few good people, much of the engineering documentation found its way to underground entities in France and other countries during the war years. Years later, the documentation was brought back to Friedrichshafen to the Zeppelinwerk's and later to the new Zeppelin Museum where I found it.

Twenty Twenty Television, London, England in 1999 produced a documentary entitled, *What happened to the Hindenburg?* The filming included some of my work up until that time. The production was shown in the US as an episode of the Public Broadcast System series *Secrets of the Dead.* As a result, I received a lot of correspondence from viewers. One letter was from a person who was part of the ground crew at the time of the disaster. He liked my theory and suggested the sparks from the engine he was standing under had possibly ignited the flammable covering. So after attending the NHA hydrogen conference in March of 2001 in Washington, DC, I drove down to meet this individual.

* * *

I met Robert (Bob) Buchanan and his wife, Betty, at their home in Kill Devil Hills, North Carolina. Bob had been under engine number 1 (aft/starboard). His description of the event is probably the most significant of all, yet goes unrecorded. The mechanics in engine car 1 did not survive to tell their story.

Bob observed engine 1 as it reversed to a forward motion and backfired, sending engine exhaust to the rear of the airship. The next thing was the fire on the starboard side up and aft over with the rear cells. Some sparking was observed with the exhaust stream.

"The fire moved forward very fast, the heat was tremendous!" he explained.

"It seemed as though the ship was drifting to our side. The heat singed my hair and neck and my clothes were steaming," he recalled.

"It was not an explosion sort of a loud puff."

Bob Buchanan

He did not recall any other engine backfiring, but was in good view of them. He had a good first view because he was intentionally looking up to catch the spider lines used for landing, but they were not dropped.

"The ship came in high, about 200 feet," he said. "I was at about a 60 degree angle exactly starboard of the engine."

We went on to discuss in more detail the behavior of the engine exhaust as it went up and over the fin on the starboard and along the aft section. The fire and sound appeared to be simultaneous from the rear. The fire then moved forward as Bob then turned and ran away from the airship.

Back at home I used my airship model at the prescribed altitude and "placed" Mr. Buchanan at the position he described. Sure enough he could have seen all engines. However, the starboard horizontal fin would have prevented him from seeing the exact location of fire initiation. Considering what was a startling event, the recalling of the fire precisely was a problem with all witnesses. Bob's observation, attesting to the general location and the timing with the exhaust stream, to me is the "smoking gun." I do not believe it was the sparks, however, that caused the fire. After all, the distance from the engine to the location in question was about 250 feet, plenty of "time for cool off." Even the Board of Inquiry concluded exhaust sparks would not be a factor for a number of reasons (low energy, fast quenching, etc.). But the exhaust particulate would posses an electrical charge as was discussed in Chapter 8. Thus the trigger.

Thank you Mr. Buchanan.

* * *

I wish to now summarize some key technical details, some of which I did not address before. There were five different weight varieties of fabric used depending on the location on the airship. All were coated with non-uniform coatings. There were at least three conditions of possible chemical reactions acting individually or in unison: The basic flammability of the doped fabric, a combination of a highly reactive fuel and oxidizer, and the ballotechnic reaction of the metallic-based dopant ingredients. The interface opening of each panel as tied to the frame was covered with fabric but did not receive the iron oxide first coat as did the adjoining panels. The non-iron oxide-doped area could exhibit a different property electrically. The very humid environment made the possibility of some panels to collect and/or disperse their electrical charge in different manners. Certain panels could conceivably accumulate enough charge as to build to a dangerous voltage level just short of electrical breakdown. The external influence of varying wind conditions and the charged engine exhaust particulate could be sufficient to precipitate discharge in a selected area or areas of the airship's envelope. I present all of these variables to illustrate the complexity to pin point the precise location of fire initiation.

To develop a timeline of significant events, I used a number of techniques. First is the flight log giving conditions in route. A drawing made by Mr. Loeser, based on 2nd officer H. Bauer's testimony of the last 20 minutes of flight, shows the approach to the mast and sequences of gas venting, ballast release and engine status.

I used my scale model of the LZ-129 and placed it at the relative altitude and location relative to a scale model of Hanger One. Eyewitnesses are identified in their respective positions. A string was used to determine line of sight and a means of measuring the distance between the observer and the event using the same scale.

Photos were also taken using the model with background conditions set up using screens, then positioning the camera shutter at the observer location. I found that the parties on the starboard side had an advantage as they were looking into the darkened background of the passing storm giving them more contrast with flame observation. The majority of viewers were on the port side but were looking into the cloud-clearing sunset in the west. There were a number of archive still photos that I arranged in sequence to get an idea of the event progress. The latter part of the event was captured on movie film so I used a stopwatch while observing the flame movement to measure the flame speed. The distance between the airship's main rings is known, so I was able to calculate flame speed by timing how long the fire took to reach each ring.

The photos showing the two tanks falling provide the information to do a reverse engineering of flame progress. That is, comparing the tank location with the flame image. The forward tank is a 2,500-liter wastewater tank at ring 198. The other tank is the 2,500-liter drinking water tank at ring 156.5. The wastewater tank at ring 77 did not dislodge. Distance can be measured on the photos of how far the tanks fell and the time interval can be calculated using the free-falling body equation. There are three photos showing the progression of the tanks falling. It is important to notice in the first photo of this series that cell one has disappeared. This provides a reference point of the relation between the events I am about to discuss.

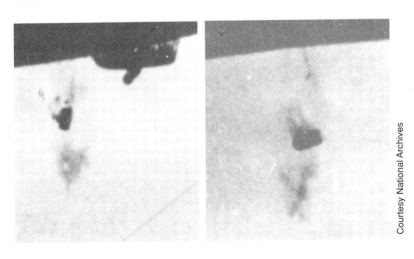

Courtesy National Archives

The book *LZ-129 Hindenburg,* by Lutz Tittel, provides information on the necessary atmospheric conditions and timing relationship during the flight. Information on temperature and relative barometric pressure provides a benchmark to calculate conditions of the airship at various times in the flight. Using the real gas laws of physics, I could calculate what the status of the gas cells were. This point is very important to determine the final status of gas cells 1 and 2, a key consideration in the analysis. Actually the condition of these cells at the time of arrival at Lakehurst can be calculated as about 90 percent full. They were not used (vented) in the final landing operation.

There were four news cameras on site, but they did not record the entire event. What was captured however helps in the analysis. The four were Pathe, Universal, Paramount and Movietone. I obtained a copy of each from the National Archives. By focusing on one point in time of the footage, some comparisons could be made and timing determined. I chose to pick the point that showed the event where the airship frame collapsed (bow area) after all cells and the outer cover were gone. This was a consistent point with all four films and then I backtracked with a chronograph to measure the time of various stages of the airship settling down. Using the frame collapse as a reference, the longest footage was by Universal at about 34 seconds.

A photo I have shows the fire in the stern area. Photographic experts indicate it appears to be a triple exposure resulting from a long shutter opening and movement by the camera operator. Computer adjustments were not successful to enhance or refine the image. Clearly though, the upper fin and the region of cell one and two is engulfed in fire. In another unpublished photo, the top of the vertical fin near the fin vent is still intact. What this tells me is the fire did not start at this point. The significance being that any internal leakage of hydrogen in the stern area would have vented out at this point, but there was no fire!

For purposes of the next discussion I need to repeat part of the Board of Inquiry testimony. Starting on page 413 of the original testimony, May 18, 1937, helmsman Helmut Lau's

Courtesy C. Ganz/B. Schneider collection

statement is documented. This particular witness is referred to because of his location on the airship at the time the fire broke out and his attention to the events observed. His location was in the bottom fin area. He described seeing a bright reflection forward of cell 4 up toward the top and on the starboard side. "At first red and yellow and there was smoke in it. Cell 4 disappeared by the heat, then 3 and 5. I saw the reflection of the fire through the cell wall ... first burning out of the fire, was on the starboard side above and, up." Lau also related the sounds he heard. Of significance is the cell bursting out on top, the strong detonation heard after the fire and cell 4 disappearing, and then cell 3 and 5. Initially he heard a sound like a "frump" as one lights a gas kitchen range. This is what he first observed causing him to look up and then the fire reflection caught his eye. The difficulty in describing exactly the sequence and relationship of events while in the midst of a conflagration is understandable.

Based on Lau's early observation, I suggest the first sound described by many "that shook forward through the ship" may have been what Lau witnessed as the bursting of the rear cells 1 and 2, causing the forward motion. The strong detonation he referred to later is consistent with the other witness reports and photos showing what appears to be cell 8 over expanding causing the well-documented upward fire plume, commonly but inaccurately labeled, "the explosion."

Further analysis indicated the bursting of cell 8 is what triggered the release of the water tanks. Hal Dick said the three water tanks were on quick release mechanisms. We speculated that the tank at ring 77 probably did not contain enough waste water to be heavy enough to dislodge. NASA did some enhanced photo imagery to show the appearance of the envelope (and hull) over the cell 8 area at selected intervals. The combination of the airship hull collapsing (a noticeable partial vacuum was observed indicating the start of an "implosion") at amidships, the framework was exposed to a rapid heat gain, the appearance of the first indication of a significant upward flame plume, the simultaneous falling of the tanks and the relationship of sound recordings timed to the event have led me to this conclusion.

Another source of data is the sound recording by Herb Morrison done at the time of the disaster. Herb Morrison's "broadcast" was recorded at the scene but was not broadcast live on a radio network, contrary to what some people think. The recording discs were taken to radio station WLS in Chicago and played from there the next day. Herb and his sidekick, Charlie Nehlsen, had to flee from German agents (as they wanted the discs) at Lakehurst to get the discs back to the station.

Also is the interesting fact that there are words missing in the 1937 airing. It seems the first sound from the disaster reached the Presto recording machine and jarred the cutting lathe. The result was a loss of a few seconds of conversation. It turns out there were two revolutions of the disc where the groove was too shallow for the replay to pick up the recording at the time.

Decade's later, thanks to Professor Biel of Morehead State University, his research uncovered the entire text. The important part of the conversation was extracted and annotated as follows:

"Its starting to rain again... the rain had slacked up a little bit ... the back motors of the ship are just holding it ...ah...just enough to keep it from ...(1) it burst into flames (2) <u>and its falling... its crashing...watch it...watch it folks get out of the way get out of the way</u> ...get this Charlie...get this Charlie its fire its crashing its crashing terrible...oh my get out of the way please its burning (3)... bursting into flames (4) and falling on the mooring mast and all the folks..."

Notes: (1) Herb sees the first burst of flames.

(2) Herb hears the sound and it is recorded on the disc. The words missing in original "broadcast" are underlined.

(3) Herb sees the second burst of flame.

(4) Herb hears the second sound and it is recorded on the disc.

The timing of the first cell bursting and the sound recording is 1.9 seconds. This matches the location/distance calculation of the sound wave velocity (it is assumed Herb was just outside of the northwest corner of hanger one). The same is true for the secondary sound at about 2.0 seconds. These data match up with the sound recording timing. Also, thanks to Professor Biel, an adjustment is made to account for the slight difference in the recording speed and the playback speed. Based on the pitch in Morrison's voice he determined that the playback was at least three percent too fast. I analyzed the resulting time difference between the two sound events to be 14.5 seconds.

Just for the record, the first live broadcast at Lakehurst that night was William Miller from a mobile unit in which he conducted interviews after the crash. But, thanks to Herb and Charlie, a valuable piece of evidence was documented.

All of this information was plotted side by side and a composite developed. Some liberty is taken on the precision of the time. Specific events would have been within a half second or so of each other so to attempt to fine tune to say a tenth of a second is sort of meaningless.

Employing the standard space launch "countdown" sequence, the following order of events is suggested. Liberty is taken to select significant points in time for the occurrence of relevant events.

T- 94 hours, 53 minutes	Liftoff in Frankfurt, Germany, with 198,000 cubic meters of hydrogen, 66 deg F, barometer 757.5 mm.
T- 65 hours, 24 minutes	Nova Scotia, 1,400 meter altitude, gas venting required as pressure height is exceeded, all cells are vented.
T- 17 minutes	Fly over mast at Lakehurst to loop the airfield, altitude 200 meters.
T- 14 minutes	First gas cell venting for landing, 15 seconds at the wheel (cells 3-14), speed 74 mph.
T- 12 minutes	Cells 12 thru 16 vented for 15 seconds.

	speed 34 mph.
T- 9 minutes	Cells 12 thru 16 vented for 15 seconds. speed 27 mph, angle of attack up 3/4 deg
T- 6 minutes	Cells 12 thru 16 vented for 5 seconds. speed 7 mph, angle of attack 0 deg, airship now lining up with the mast.
T- 4 minutes	Airship stationary, altitude 90 meters, bow ropes dropped.
T- 2.5 minutes	Bow ropes become conductive due to high humidity (Bureau of Commerce data) airship frame equalizes with ground potential.
T- 30 seconds	Gust of wind port side.
T- 10/5 seconds	Engine one, short run to compensate for port wind, backfire and exhaust plume to aft with negative charged carbon particulate is speculated. *Folks, this was the smoking gun.*
T- 3 seconds	First sign of electrical activity observed aft starboard rear of upper fin.
T- 2 seconds	Electrostatic behavior begins, electron flow occurs within one or more panels at quadrant of rings 15.5 to 29 and longitudinals of 12 to 16.
T- 1 second	Electron flow triggers reaction of chemical elements in envelope doping compounds.
T- 0	Envelope ignites in the stern starboard quadrant providing a high temperature intense flame moving

<table>
<tr><td></td><td>rapidly across the outer part of cell 1 and areas of cell 2.</td></tr>
<tr><td>T+1.5 sec</td><td>Cell 1 (with contents of cell 2 interconnected with cell 1) bursts aft due to thermal expansion of hydrogen gas (per calculations they were initially at least 90% full, relief valve in cell 2 does not handle the overpressure) flames rise 40 feet high behind upper fin (not yet directly observable by port observers, but they do see a red glow). Hydrogen begins role in the fire fuel equation.</td></tr>
<tr><td>T+ 5.0 sec</td><td>Fire progresses on starboard side, Cell 4 starts to melt, fire observed momentarily forward of upper fin, flames shoot 100 feet high across top rear cells. Fire breaks through to the port side forward of the fin as evidenced in an unpublished photo.</td></tr>
<tr><td>T+ 8.0 sec</td><td>Cell 3 melts, as flames engulf the stern area and then proceed forward.</td></tr>
<tr><td>T+ 10.0 sec</td><td>Cell 5 melts.</td></tr>
<tr><td>T+ 12.0 sec</td><td>Cell 6 melts.</td></tr>
<tr><td>T+ 14.0 sec</td><td>Cell 7 melts.</td></tr>
<tr><td>T+ 16 sec</td><td>Cell 8 is compressed from action of the annulus (space between outer cover and the cells inside) at lower than atmospheric pressure (semi-vacuum of less dense, very hot air) causing initial fracture of the airframe at the same time internal cell gas pressure rises</td></tr>
</table>

from the intense heat. Strong upward air convection currents are created. The combination of all these forces result in an upward burst of the cell, its contents and the destruction of the surrounding structure causing sufficient force to dislodge two water tanks.

T+ 17.2 sec   A mushroom flame front forms above cell 8 at about 140 feet rising rapidly. The two tanks fall to 23 feet below the airship.

T+ 19.2 sec   The tanks have now fallen 89 feet below the hull. The flames rise 200 feet high.

T+ 21 sec   Cell 9 starts to melt

T+ 22 sec   Tanks hit the ground, flames are now 380 feet high.

T+ 24 sec   Cell 10 starts to melt, flames accelerate to over 800 feet high.

T+ 25 sec   Lower fin hits ground.

T+ 26 sec   Aft section of airship collapses. Bow is at upward angle of 45 degrees, fire breaks out of bow to about 75 feet, cell 16 breached, flames still about 800 feet, breaks up and disperse outward.

T+ 27 sec   Bow rises to 72 degrees, cell 15 breached, flame out bow is 175 feet, flames overall retract to 390 feet high, cell 11 and 12 also breached.

T+ 36 sec   Bow lowers to 40 degrees, flames at 200 feet. cell 13 and 14 breached.

T+ 42 sec	Bow at 20 degrees, flames 200 feet, bow engulfed in flame, slight bounce when front wheel hits the ground, indicative of residual buoyancy in some cells.
T+ 48 sec	Entire forward structure is engulfed in flame.
T+ 52 sec	Frame collapses, fire 50 feet high, black smoke towers 1,000 feet over the site.

As we see, it's all over within less than a minute. The three million dollar luxury airship becomes a pile of rubble.

The New York Times had the following in the next day's edition:

"At 8 o'clock this morning the mass of debris that once was the graceful Hindenburg was still smouldering [sic], and reporters who were given the opportunity to get close to the twisted wreckage noted an acrid odor emanating from the ruins. Wires, struts and girders were bent and misshapen, turned and twisted in every direction."

* * *

Ok, let's take a look at the hydrogen theory next, see if you believe, really believe this one.

The flutter of the cover, the appearance of a tail heavy condition, the radical sharp turn made by Capt Pruss shortly before approaching the mast, the constant cross examination of crew members, "Did you smell hydrogen?" the suggestion of the interrogator, "Did you not hear a pop before the fire?" constituted the relentless search for evidence that hydrogen was the culprit.

First is the need for the correct proportion of air and hydrogen. Too lean a mixture (more air) is probably not a condition, but less than a rich (more hydrogen) mixture was difficult, but is an acceptable condition for consideration.

Next is to provide an electrical or other energy source to be at the exact spot at the exact time.

Then assure the dwell time is sufficient such that the "fire" does not just result in a momentary flash and the burnable mix is spent before the very low radiant heat could set off the secondary incendiary nature of the other nearby flammable materials.

Possible? Well let's assume possible.

The official Board of Inquiry report concluded that the one key element was the presence of static electricity and high probability of an electrical arc occurring. This does not seem to be an issue of debate among historians and experts in the field. So let us accept that idea.

Logic suggests that for whatever reason hydrogen had to escape and combine with air to establish a proper combustible mixture. So let us accept that idea. Whether it was a broken wire, a bullet hole, renting of a gas cell due to rubbing on the metal frame, or a gas cell vent valve slightly stuck open, or some other factor does not really matter for our purposes right now.

What is going to happen with free hydrogen? If in a vent shaft then it will rise to the top out of the vent hood to the open air. Call this case 1. If inside the airship, it will rise to the top and exit out of the annulus vent hood to the open air. Call this case 2. It can mix with sufficient air present in the space between the cells and outer envelope. Call this, case 3. The mix of hydrogen and air within a gas cell can be dismissed because the amount of air needed to form a combustible mix

1. Common hull vent.
2. Cell 1, 2, 3 vent.
3. Finvent.

is so large that it would affect the lift and would have been noticed by the crew.

Case 1. I have the drawings of the hull so I know the exact configuration of the vent shafts. Being very conservative, I assumed a mix of 4% hydrogen flowing in the shaft by some small leak of a valve. The flowing gas rose to the vent hood. This had to be the vent hood between cell four and five. Cell 1, 2 and 3 have their common vent on the lower part of each side of the upper fin. In order to maintain the flow, I calculated that within the 2% sensitivity of the gas cell manometer, operators at the monitoring panel would have detected a decrease in cell volume in under a minute. I built a model of the vent hood and applied a flow of hydrogen. The experiment was captured on video. The first event was to check that hydrogen was indeed flowing using a gas detection meter. Then a static spark generator was used to

Gas detection

Arc ignition

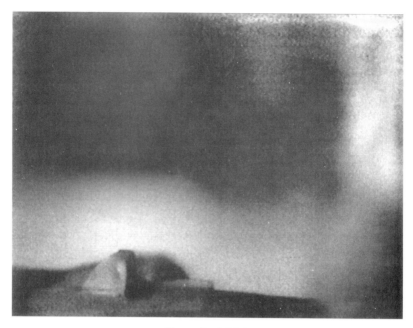

Flame (invisible)

Proof of flame

trigger a spark across the vent hood. I knew we had a flame as I put my hand above the hood at about three feet and felt the heat. Considering the flame was above the reflective material of the vent hood and because of hydrogen's low radiation nothing happened. In order to show on film that a fire existed I used a piece of paper and slowly brought it to within a few inches above the hood. The paper caught fire. I lowered it trying to determine how close the hydrogen flame was to the hood, I got too close and the fabric on the hood started to burn as my very radiant carbon based fire ignited the flammable fabric. So much for the idea that the *Hindenburg* fire started forward of the upper fin.

Case 2. The same thing would happen as in case 1. The annulus was afforded several vents along the top of the airship. As previously discussed, airship experts indicated the *Hindenburg* had a very good ventilation system. This applies to cells forward of the fins. The three aft cells had a different vent configuration. It should also be pointed out that within the confines of the metal airframe there would have been no static related discharges due to the Faraday Cage effect. This is analogous to the principle that you are protected from lightning while in a car due to the metal shield around you.

Since the fire apparently originated further aft, this brings us to a different scenario in the next case.

Case 3. If for whatever reason hydrogen was escaping out of cell 1, 2 or 3, it of course would want to rise to the top under the envelope cover. But at the bottom of the upper fin over these same cells the frame is not covered. The hydrogen logically would go up into the upper fin. The designers purposely put vent hoods on both sides at the top of the fin. They knew there would be some hydrogen resulting from the permeability of the gas cell material. Thus the vents permitted

the gas to escape. I built a 1:80 scale model of the top stern section of LZ-129. It included a small "rip" in cell 4, vent hood at cell 4 and 5, and the vents at the top of the fin. Applying a flow of hydrogen to the rip, hydrogen was detected coming out the vent hood as well as the vents on the fin as would have been expected.

So lets take the situation of hydrogen venting out the upper fin vents. It is a very logical location for St. Elmo's or other electrical discharge to occur. Not only that, but the vent hoods are horizontal. So if I applied my vent hood fire model to this configuration, fabric ignition would occur because of flame impingement on the surface... but back to the evidence. A photo taken many seconds after the fire started shows the upper tip of the fin still intact. The area in question at this point was not on fire.

The other experiment was to take a piece of the 60-year-old fabric and run hydrogen permeability tests. To my surprise the hydrogen actually had to be under a slight pressure in order to penetrate the fabric. I am sure over a period of time one can expect some leak through, but that requires some sort of pocket to build up a little positive pressure. The surface over the cells under discussion has an upward slope of about 15 degrees lengthwise as well as the top section sideways. Thus the "leaking" hydrogen would be channeled to the nearest vents quite easily, not going through the fabric.

Creating a condition of some undetected loss of hydrogen at a very specific spot at a proper mix ratio with air and to encounter a sufficient spark at the exact same spot explains why Hitler declared it an "Act of God." Indeed, the Almighty would pretty much have to be involved for such a string of unlikely events to happen in the precise order required.

Thus any hydrogen theory in the past, now, or in the future, must yield to a very well developed sequence of events and justified situational conditions while maintaining the laws of hydrogen behavior, ignition and electrostatic discharge phenomena.

There are still, and will always be, believers in the hydrogen theory. I hope in time the nonbelievers overwhelm the believers.

Mishaps with flying the various airships led the designers and engineers to continually improve their airship. Many technical problems were not uncovered until an incident occurred. In some cases the real problem was not uncovered until years later. In some cases the suspected cause, or causes, were identified in a short time. Such is the case with all of man's marvelous machines. Let us look at three events over the last 100 years that will continue to be brought to our attention on their infamous anniversaries.

In the case of the *Titanic* disaster, the presumption persisted for decades that simple pilot error, miscommunication among the crew, and lack of sophisticated modern-day electronic surveillance and detection equipment sufficed as the concluding explanation. Having been outfitted with the electronic gear mentioned, perhaps the Titanic would have sailed for years without its crew's knowledge that it was a floating disaster destined to happen at a time of appropriate environmental conditions.

The largest ship built to date, luxurious, with all the apparent attention to engineering detail, virtually unsinkable, the ultimate in turn-of-the-century technology; yet the question remained to some as to why she sank so fast. Eyewitness accounts describe the event as a casual rubbing of the starboard hull with a wall of ice.

"Designed" to take at least three days to sink in case of the worst imaginable catastrophe (head on collision with another ship), the *Titanic* slipped beneath the cold water's surface, carrying more than 1,500 passengers, in less than three hours. The submergence equation had a missing unknown not to be found for years. Fortunately the later ships were built with better steels unaware that this may have been the problem with the *Titanic*.

In 1985 the *Titanic* remains were located and in 1991 samples of the steel hull were recovered and tested. Subjected to the Charpy V-notch test for ductility, it was found that the high sulfur steel plate and rivets were very brittle. Adding to the ductility problem was the environmental factor as the water temperature at the location of the disaster was one degree F above freezing. Typically, certain classes of steel lose their strength as the surrounding temperature is decreased. Another theory is that the heads of the rivets may have been overstressed. For a mechanical/chemical engineer, the solution to the equation descriptive of a tragic event had been satisfied.

Thus we see a materials science problem coupled with

just the right (wrong) environmental situation at the unfortunate precise moment. Otherwise, the *Titanic* may have sailed for years.

The Space Shuttle, the most highly technological machine ever built, brings into play practically every engineering and scientific discipline. The enormous talent base this represents was fortunately available to rapidly solve the equation descriptive of the 1986 *Challenger* disaster. Nevertheless, before it was concluded that a solid rocket booster O-ring failed materially in the cold temperature environment existing prior to launch, the media conjectured that the onboard hydrogen fuel was at the root of the cause.

Despite the fact that the Space Shuttle carries six and a half times the hydrogen as was onboard the *Hindenburg*, it was proved not to be a causation factor, but did contribute to the conflagration effect, as did other onboard propellants. The role of hydrogen in the disaster still perpetuates the idea that hydrogen is too dangerous. For the *Challenger*, like the *Hindenburg*, hydrogen was necessary.

Thus we see a materials science problem coupled with the right (wrong) environmental situation at the unfortunate precise moment. Otherwise, the *Challenger* may have flown for years.

The *Hindenburg* incident, a minor aircraft accident compared to subsequent air disasters and lives lost, but a major event because of its spectacular impression and media coverage, continues to perpetuate the myth that hydrogen is unacceptably dangerous. The Zeppelin Company and other investigations by laboratories in Germany concluded that the combination of the doped outer cover design flaw and the circumstances at Lakehurst prompted the incident.

Thus we see a materials science problem coupled with the

right (wrong) environmental situation at the unfortunate precise moment. Otherwise, the *Hindenburg* may have flown for years.

The fundamental cause and effect of these events are all similar, each an example of the frailty of human engineering. Either through the lack of appropriate materials testing, or selection and technical communication, all of these disasters can be attributed to a common phenomenon the materials incompatibility of the machine with the given operational environment.

Like the ocean liner industry, like the aerospace industry, and like the airship industry, the machines are designed with the latest and best technology incorporated. The Zeppelin Company has taken these new technologies to get back into the airship business once again. Their latest version is the "NT" for new technology. It is small compared with the LZ-129 but it is very nice inside. I cannot wait to someday take a ride. The NT's use helium, but who knows if that will always be so.

There have been a number of proposals to consider hydrogen again for airships. For starters, there are ideas to use hydrogen for engine fuel. Other ideas resurrect the idea of using hydrogen as the variable lift gas, and preserving the helium for use as the static element.

Clearly the technology is there, but is the public ready? I don't think so. I sincerely believe that one day the public will be ready as it gets more conditioned to using hydrogen in their cars and at home. I am working with companies considering airships for forest fire fighting concepts as well as a company that has a very effective and environmentally friendly product to combat fires. The combination may have significant impact to control forest fires if augmented with the normal policy of the Forest Service. That is, "a let it burn" policy is the preferred practice to allow the fuel that is built up on the forest "floor" to burn and let Mother Nature take its course.

Well, that is ok until things get out of control and houses and lives are threatened. Airplanes and helicopters delivering flame-retardants have limited affect. An airship can concentrate the flame combatant to the proper location and observe the effectiveness in real time. On board detection equipment could provide monitoring of hot spots or other conditions of the progressing wildland fire. Of importance is to allow for the less dense hot air above a fire, as that would affect the airship buoyancy.

So, that leads me to the humorous suggestion that I made, tongue in cheek, to some colleagues. Fly the airship on hydrogen over a raging forest fire.

Of course they balk! They don't know what you the reader now knows…the pure hydrogen inside of the airship won't burn and any venting would be above the airship. The hydrogen would rapidly disperse upward.

* * *

In summary, for the exoneration of hydrogen, I am reminded of the following.

The log kept by the Lakehurst Air Station had the following entry. "During landing operation, the airship Hindenburg burst into flame at an altitude of about 200 feet and was burned to destruction by hydrogen fire originating at or near the stern."

The officer who made that log entry took it upon himself to condemn the lifting gas, without a trial, or even a hearing. We members of the human race tend to form an opinion based on first impression or initial suggestion. If a person were arrested on suspicion of a crime, human nature would tend to agree with the first accusation.

Therefore, our Founding Fathers wisely instituted a Constitutional guarantee that a person is presumed innocent until proven guilty. We have long since forgotten or never knew that nothing more than rumor or hearsay, not a scintilla of evidence to convict hydrogen, was ever presented. The argument is outcome-based: There was a fire, hydrogen mixed with air will burn, there must have been a leak, and there must have been a spark, no mystery here, what's to explain?

Folk's, I guess only God knows precisely what happened that fateful day. I believe my theory to be a compelling theory based on a methodical examination of all sources of information. I make no claim it is the answer, but I have yet to see any better one. At the time the investigative board(s) did not have the sophisticated investigative tools of today. Since 1937, much more has been learned about the nature of hydrogen behavior. The science of electrostatic discharge (ESD) is relatively new. The reactive behavior of the compounds in the makeup of the doping compounds used only became known fifty years after the disaster. The board(s) spent less than thirty days to form their conclusion.

I spent a decade.

Will there be more theories proposed in the future? Probably. Are the critics satisfied? No. A professor at Texas A&M bombarded me for months with specific questions. Having heard no more, I assume I have answered his questions. Short of being slanderous, a professor at the University of Arizona suggests the "paint theory" as not only flawed, but fatally flawed. His own paper is flawed in many ways. Okay, so what really happened at 7:25 PM at the Lakehurst airfield on May 6, 1937? The professor did not touch that question.

Chapter 10

Going Public

Richard Van Treuren was following the progress of my studies closely. An avid writer, he suggested it was time to get something published. He had established a contact at the Smithsonian that was interested in putting an article in their magazine. It went well as we were able to pretty much dictate what went in the article. It was published in May, 1997.

Shortly afterward, *Popular Science* was at my doorstep to expand on an article on airships they were planning for the November 1997 issue. The *Hindenburg* write up started out as an "inset" to the main article. When it went to the editor things changed and it became a feature article with it announced on the front cover. I was promised that I could review the copy before publication. This was the beginning of my experience on how publishers tend to not "allow sources " to influence the final outcome. As a result, the final article had eleven errors. One was a glaring oversight—the fact that the airship was originally designed for both helium and hydrogen and that was not the final configuration.

Well, all hell broke loose with counter articles, emails, letters, phone calls and so forth, but all in all I would say 95% of the contacts were positive. It prompted inquiries and resulting requests for interviews, presentations and offers to make TV documentaries. That's all I needed to interfere with my continuing work on the topic, since I still had some loose ends about the research bothering me at the time.

* * *

I don't recall how many times our house was invaded. Lights, sound, cameras, cables all over the damn place and then take, retake and retake. I now really feel sorry for actors, except for their big bucks. Where in the hell were my attorneys, financial experts and agent? Well, for this Montana boy things were growing like a snowball coming down Big Mountain at the ski lodge north of Kalispell. Eventually a little compensation began to put things in perspective... my "fifteen minutes of fame" had arrived.

First was the company from Germany, Dr. Peter Bardehle Enterprises, then the Canadian Discovery Channel closely followed by the US Discovery Channel. Next 20/20 Channel 4 London, followed by *National Geographic* and of course local newspapers and national magazines. There were a number of radio interviews such as Voice of America. I believe the best documentary was Dan Clifton's (20/20) rendering that is now part of the PBS series *Secrets of the Dead*. I do wish I had the opportunity to review and edit the film before release to clarify some points, but that is the way it is! Dan later told me they dropped some of the finer technical details and took liberty with the presentation pointing out that the show was for the general public, not the technocrats.

Over the years I have collected statements from newspaper and magazine articles and books making statements about the *Hindenburg* disaster. I would like to share with you the extent and variation of these accounts. I have selected a few, and I mean few, from my library, but these are the most interesting to me. Note I have not corrected any grammar or misspelling in the quotes. I have tried to group the quotes in a topic format and then follow with my comments.

"The giant Hindenburg explodes killing all 100 people on board"

New York Times, 1937

"The inferno of blazing hydrogen gas cremates all living beings in its path as the twisted skeleton of the balloon settles quickly to the ground"

Universal Newspaper, 1937

"Lakehurst Zep Blast Kills 80"

Daily News, NYC, 1937

"Interestingly, only about a dozen people were killed in the Hindenburg accident, yet doomed the airship as a means of air transport. If the same logic had been applied to airline travel, people would not be flying today."

Future Flight, McGraw-Hill, 1994

" For example, in a very famous disastrous accident of Hindenburg at Lakehurst 1937, 36 people died, while another 65 people were survived because who were located under side of the airoship house and did not exposed to the radiant heat"

Safety of Hydrogen, report by Musashi Institute of Technology

Comment. There were 97 people on board. Of the 61 crewmembers, 39 survived. Of the 36 passengers 23 survived. One ground crew member was killed.

"It was probably static electricity that traveled up the wet landing ropes and ignited the gas being valved off. Others blamed lightning, St. Elmo's fire, or even sabotage. But the true reason was flammable hydrogen"

Up, Up and Away: The Story of Ballooning,
Westminster Press, 1980

<u>Comment.</u> There had been no valving of hydrogen for six minutes prior to the fire breakout. The frame acquired the same potential of the ground once the bow ropes became conductive. The ropes were attached to the underside of the airship; the vent hoods were at the top of the airship. The fire started in the stern, not the top.

"The fire was spectacular but hydrogen is less dangerous than the *Hindenburg* conflagration made it appear – the victims died by falling, not burning. Because the gas is light, it rises as soon as it is freed from the envelope, so the fire, burning very rapidly, moves upwards and away from the people below."

Elements: Air, Facts on File, 1992

"Some 7 million cubic feet of hydrogen escaped upward before the Hindenburg crashed to the ground. No person lost their life because of hydrogen burns."

American Hydrogen Association newsletter, 1999

"The 36 who died were killed in the fall, not from burning hydrogen, which simply floated away."

Los Angeles Times, 1995

"What really caused the loss of life was the diesel fuel igniting and then spreading to the canvass cover that was not flameproofed. Of all the deaths there were none due to hydrogen burns. All the deaths were caused by either diesel burns or from people jumping to their deaths."

Clean Air Now, 1998

"Most of the passengers who remained onboard the dirigible survived. Another victim belonged to the ground personnel and was killed by a falling Diesel engine. Most burns were caused by leaking Diesel oil and not by burning hydrogen."

Liquid Hydrogen: Fuel of the Future, Springer-Verlaz/Wien, 1992

Comment. Perhaps a mute point, but the residual hydrogen in the airship prior to the landing attempt was about five and a half million cubic feet not the full capacity of seven million.

In a matter of a few seconds after fire initiation and the breaching of the gas cells one by one, hydrogen became part of the complex fire equation and continued to do so until many seconds after the bow of the airship hit the ground. Clearly the black and white photos show a mixing of the various components of burning airship materials and hydrogen.

According to the coroner's (Dr. Raymond Taylor) report on each of the victims, the statement is made, "cause of death due to severe burns." People did jump, some ran away. Some may have been knocked unconscious, others asphyxiated as the burning airship crashed on them.

Nine of the twelve crewmembers in the bow perished. As the bow pointed skyward during the airship's descent, flames engulfed and shot out of the bow. One member fell, perhaps already dead. It was caught on film. As one crewmember told me, the fire was just swishing above his head toward the front as he held to keep from falling backward into the fire. It seems logical the multi-fueled flames in this attitude contained a high concentration of hydrogen molecules. At this point the airship is 90% history. There is no evidence that an engine fell on the ground crew member (Allen Hagaman) who perished. According to a witness, he ran and stumbled over a rail as the airship crashed around him. Another witness indicated Mr. Hagaman may have become confused and ran towards the falling airship. The engines were several hundred feet from his position.

Most of the diesel fuel storage tankage was concentrated near the engines about two hundred feet behind the passenger compartment. This fuel started to become part of the fire equation when the aft end hit the ground and created the thick black smoke. The four crewmembers in the aft section however escaped unharmed. Fuel from the few tanks in the forward section would contribute to the fire after the rest of the airship hit the ground. At this point, the 26 victims at the scene would already be dead. The other victims died later in nearby hospitals.

Crewmembers Eugene Schaeble, Fritz Deeg, Willi Zalla and Hans Frund jumped. Their pictures are in the newspaper the next day showing them walking around, albeit a bandage or so here and there. Passengers Leonhardt and Gertrude Adelt, Otto Clemens and George Grant jumped and survived without serious injury. Matilda Doehner threw her three children out the open window, and then she slid down a rope until her hands were rope burned, then she fell the rest of the way. She and the two boys were in the hospital a short time. Fourteen-year-old Irene, her daughter, died from severe burns later in the hospital. As one newspaper article noted, "Most of the 17 (survivors in hospitals) were almost completely encased in seemingly endless strips of gauze bandage. Several had plaster casts about their feet or arms–mute indications that they had escaped more severe burns by desperate leaps from the flaming Zeppelin" (*New York Evening Journal*, May 8, 1937).

"Remember the Hindenberg! A giant flaming sausage dangling from a mooring mast in Lakehurst. Hydrogen! Mysteriously ignited by a semi-superstitious thing called St. Elmo's fire. Now, liquid hydrogen; another penetration into the hitherto unknown, associated with H-bombs and radioactive fallout."

Air Products Cryogenic Safety
manual (1960)

Comment. Hindenburg is misspelled, as it frequently is. The airship never reached the mooring mast, therefore it did not "dangle." There is no acceptable evidence that St. Elmo's was the ignition source.

"On its eleventh crossing of the Atlantic from Europe to Lakehurst, New Jersey in 1937, it had some 100 passengers and crew members. As the people began to disembark, a fire started in the balloon. Nobody knows for sure how the fire started: some say it was because of a malfunction in an electrical contact; others say it was sabotage."

*Solar Hydrogen Energy: The Power
to save the Earth*, Optima, 1991

Comment. The 63rd trip of the airship was the seventh crossing from Europe to Lakehurst. The airship never landed, therefore people could not disembark. The electrical contact and sabotage theories were discounted well before this 1991 publication.

Popular Science, October 2001, article on the Fuel Cell Bike. "On second thought hydrogen has an unpleasant tendency to explode."

Comment. It requires the proper amount of air mixed with hydrogen and a proper amount of energy for the mixture to "explode." And then in a somewhat confined environment. (Total mass of the mix is a factor as well).

The New York Times, February 2001, Children's Books, "Like its sister metaphor the Titanic, the Hindenburg has become a colossal monument to dimwitted hubris, its destruction remembered less as an instant of epic sorrow than as a teachable moment for all humanity. Or, as any 8-year-old can explain: if you are going to cross the ocean, go slow and look both ways for icebergs, unless you are attached to a giant bag of explosive gas, in which case – pray."

Comment. No comment!

Natural Gas Fuels, 7/2000, advertisement by Schwinn bikes, "At Schwinn, we want every ride to be memorable. But we still recommend you fill your tires with air rather than highly flammable hydrogen gas. In fact, in 1934, Schwinn made it company policy to never weld aboard hydrogen-filled airships."

Comment. A little silly isn't it?

"Today, of course, thanks to the educational efforts of the bottled-water industry, we consumers are terrified of our tap water, because we know that it contains some of the most deadly substances known to man: chemicals. To cite one example: Bottled-water industry researchers recently issued an alarming report stating that virtually every sample of tap water they tested contained large quantities of hydrogen, which is a type of atom believed to have caused the Hindenburg dirigible disaster. This is why millions of consumers now prefer bottled water."

Orlando Sentinel, August 2002

<u>Comment.</u> This is one of the most stupid things ever written (about hydrogen).

From Ben Jordan. "Addison's scholarly rebuttal of the years of hydrogen mythomania, should go far toward dispelling society's irrational fears of hydrogen's danger. Hydrogen advocates will applaud your efforts to set the record straight but will decry your failure to <u>shout</u> 'Forget the Hindenburg!' loud enough. Say it again! And again!"

From Sandy Thomas. "I was scanning through my daughter's college chemistry book last week, and came upon this picture of the Hindenburg. Naturally I thought of you when I saw the unambiguous caption on the picture that the extreme flammability of hydrogen 'caused its destruction.' How's that for objectivity? The text had no mention of hydrogen's safety record. To think that generations of young men and women are being taught to link hydrogen with the Hindenburg – at the college level, no less. You have your work cut out for you."

Sandy makes a good point about students continuing to be taught to link hydrogen with the *Hindenburg*. Not long ago I saw a book on the *Hindenburg* in the young adult section of the local library. Reading through it, I came upon the statement about the dangerous hydrogen causing the disaster. I immediately went to the front to see what the copyright date was. It was 2001.

In my own backyard is a newspaper called *Florida Today*. It covers events associated with the space coast. The reporters are very familiar with the Space Shuttle details and lingo. They know that MECO means main engine cut off. When there is a technical problem on the Space Shuttle involving hydrogen it goes something like this; "Engineers at the space center experienced a leak in a vent line that carries the highly explosive liquid hydrogen." They never mention the highly explosive liquid oxygen, which is closer to being factual.

I guess I would expect the news media to continue to report scary news, after all, it sells. The scientists however sometimes do clever things to avoid scary things. For example, ever have an "MRI"? The magnetic resonance imaging machine was first called nuclear magnetic resonance, but the public conditioning to fear the word "nuclear" resulted in a name change. Would you slip your body into a nuclear machine? Probably not. Public fear of the unknown is irrational, but real.

I took a bus tour of the space center with a friend not long ago. As part of the tour there is a stop at an observation tower where one can get a good look at the Complex 39 launch pads. On the first floor there is a model of the Space Shuttle on the pad with the Rotating Service Structure (RSS). The rollback of the RSS is demonstrated along with how the vented oxygen is captured in what is called a beanie cap and carried safely away. Then, on the TV screen they show how the *dangerous explosive hydrogen,* (as they call it) that is also vented is carried away. I believe about three million people from around the world take the tour every year. NASA, can't you simply say flammable hydrogen?

I do find pleasurable reporting on occasions. For example, I saw a book on the newsstand by *Readers Diges*t entitled, *How Did It Really Happen?* The book, published in 2000, includes a write up of the *Hindenburg* disaster on page 242. It covers the research I did in a positive manner.

At a hydrogen conference in Washington in 2002 someone made the statement that we don't need to worry about the *Hindenburg* anymore. In essence, no one writes about it. Well, I mentioned the fact that more books keep coming out on the subject, especially in the young adult section of the library. Since that conference, I have noticed at least two books a year. Some still site hydrogen, but others are supporting my investigation.

The Hindenburg, by author Gina De Angelis is a recent book. A very good write up, especially about the rebirth of airships. Ms. De Angelis, if you read this, please next time change the sentence on page 13. "Hydrogen, unlike helium, is flammable. (Thank you for not saying highly flammable) When mixed with even a tiny amount of ordinary air, it becomes explosive." Hopefully you will correct this. By the way, thank you for not just showing the flaming airship in color on your book cover.

Just when I thought the students would be getting better information here comes a book by *Capstone Press,* author Ms. Deady, copyright 2003, even though I bought it in November 2002. The two dozen-page book, mostly with photos, discusses the hydrogen explosion a number of times. There are several technical and historical errors in the book, although the author indicates there was consultation by the Navy Lakehurst Historical Society. Too bad, really.

In a recent book by environmental physiologist Dr. Robert Siblerud, *Our Future Is Hydrogen!,* he states on page 83, "Experts now understand that not one person died from the hydrogen fire, but almost all of the fatalities occurred as a result of people jumping to the ground. A recent study by a NASA investigator has shown that hydrogen did not contribute to the severity of the disaster." Oh boy, here we go again about the people. And the hydrogen? Now where in the hell did over a billion Btu's of energy go?

The "NASA investigator," claims it was not necessary for the hydrogen to *initiate* the fire. Lets get the record straight.

I do hope future authors study what an explosion really is before using the term recklessly. Consider the explanation provided by the four-crew members in the lower fin of the airship. They were the closest to the event. Lau, Freund, Sauter and Kollmer say in consensus, "not a sharp detonation, more of a 'frump,' "muffled detonation," "detonation like the firing of a small gun." What they relate to is in fact the instant heating and subsequent over pressurization of cell one and two as they burst aft.

Hydrogen was blamed for the deaths. With endless repetition of the words and picture accompaniment for this accusation [we've set aside the Constitution of the United Sates for the element accused in this case.] Not the greatest aircraft disaster, but the newsreel crews were there. Herb Morrison was there. So, for sixty years and probably on every May 6 in the future, the pictures and words are still there.

It is interesting what the passengers on board have said. German Ambassador to the US, Dr. Hans Luther, visited those in the hospital. He has said, "You would have thought those people would recoil from the thought of further travel in that manner, but almost without exception they were insistent the awful catastrophe should not destroy confidence in such ships."

Margaret Unger, one of the 25 booked for the return flight to Europe that fateful night, and having witnessed first hand the fire, said, "I would go on a dirigible in a minute, even if it were filled with hydrogen. I think that it was just an unfortunate accident."

Air Minister Hermann Goering, Chancellor and Hitler's right hand man, dramatically dispatched orders, May 8, to the giant Zeppelin making base at Friedrichshafen to speed up at once the work of the LZ-130, then nearing completion.

* * *

My last "going public" entry is something I found in a 1937 newspaper, part of a collection of papers I purchased from a collector. Actually the papers were part of a file I meant to get back to later as it contained a lot about who the people were and was not part of the research. Before retiring the file, I decided to read through all the pages. There in the yellowed and tattered page was a short paragraph. The headline was, "Spark from motor ignited hydrogen is advanced as cause." Probably this is why I set the paper aside for so long. Newsman Herbert Rau of the *Lakewood Daily Times* continues without reference to any source: "Outer skin of the ship's body was a cotton material, made weather tight by means of coatings of aluminum powder 'dope.' It is believed that sparks from a kicking motor permeated this aluminum powder. The sparks then ignited, it was said, the easily inflammable cotton material. It was an easy matter for the rapidly spreading flames to reach the hydrogen cells." The Board of Inquiry discounted the sparks, of course, as having insufficient energy to ignite any materials, including hydrogen, but they did not say much about the outer skin, and certainly nothing alluding to the possible role of the aluminum powder.

Interesting! Where did the press get the information? I wonder…

Chapter 11

The New Label

The plaque, or label, as the Smithsonian prefers to phrase it, bothered me for years. I kept reviewing it and of course the first priority was to convince the institution that the phrase "It's hydrogen exploded" needed to be reworded. I then noticed other errors in the description as I became more knowledgeable about the airship. First was the proper date of the *Hindenburg* completion and the other was the fact that it could carry 72 passengers rather than the 50 stated. The passenger cabins had been expanded from 50 to 72 for the 1937 season.

The National Hydrogen Association held their 9th Annual Meeting the spring of 1998 in Washington D.C. Senator Tom Harkin, "Mr. Hydrogen," as he is called on the Hill, has supported hydrogen for years and had been invited to give a speech at the meeting. At the end he looked to the audience for comments. I could not have asked for a better straight man when someone in the audience, someone I did not know, raised up and said, "But Senator, what about the Hindenburg?"

"Well," he said, " Yes I understand it may not have been the hydrogen but the diesel fuel on board."

I could not resist. I could feel the eyes staring at me from those that knew of my work.

I stood up, "Senator, sorry to contradict you but it was something else."

So he went on to ask what my explanation was.

"The airship was coated with rocket fuel," I blurted out.

There were over 300 people in attendance. I really intended to be more humorous than contentious.

Senator Harkin and his legislative assistant met with me immediately afterward. I went on to explain that the results of my work were detailed in a November 1997 edition of Popular Science. I sent him an autographed copy, inscribed, "To Senator Tom Harkin, may your efforts accelerate the inevitable hydrogen future, Addison Bain."

To my surprise the Senator took the steps to place the entire article in the Congressional Record (S11631 October 6, 1998) with a very nice preamble. Standing at the podium, the Senator spoke, "Mr. President, for many years I have spoken of the promise of hydrogen energy as our best hope for an environmentally safe sustainable energy future."

He continued later with, "I would like to personally thank Addison Bain for his valuable contribution to the history of the Hindenburg, and to lessening the public's concerns over the safety of hydrogen."

I seized the opportunity of now being on a one-to-one communication basis with the Senator and told him about the plaque at the model of the *Hindenburg* in the National Air and Space Museum (NASM) depicting some false and incomplete information. He wrote a letter to the director of NASM dated January 25, 1999 and in essence it stated, "I strongly encourage you to correct this small, yet vital scientific fact."

The folks at NASM and myself over several months fine tuned versions of a new label until we were both happy with the final inscription. At the time this was going on, the museum gift shop was under going remodeling, so the model had been put into temporary storage. When the model was re-hung just outside of the new gift shop the new label was ready. The following is how it is now worded.

Hindenburg
1/28-scale model

Built by Germany's Luftschiffbau Zeppelin Company, LZ-129 *Hindenburg* entered passenger service in 1936. The airship could carry 72 passengers and a crew of 54 and was powered by four 1,000 horsepower Daimler-Benz diesel engines. When fully inflated, its 16 gas cells held some 200,000 cubic meters (260,000 cubic yards) of hydrogen.

Hindenburg crossed the North and South Atlantic safely several times. Then late in the afternoon of May 6, 1937, the airship burst into flames as it approached the mooring mast at the U.S. Naval Air Station in Lakehurst, New Jersey. The conflagration may have begun when static electricity ignited the airship's highly flammable outer covering. Of the 97 passengers and crew, 62 survived.

Universal City Studios built this model to use in its feature film, *Hindenburg.*

Lent by Universal City Studios, Inc.

Senator Harkin and fabric

LZ-129 Model, Smithsonian

My work is still not done, as I have a proposed project in which I envision a display case near the label that will contain the many *Hindenburg* artifacts that I have accumulated in addition to items that have been promised by other collectors with whom I have made contact. Preliminary coordination with NASM has been initiated … but part of the deal will be for a copy of this book to also be displayed!

Chapter 12

Hydrogen Realities

For most people, the mere mention of the word "hydrogen" scares up images of the *Hindenburg* disaster and the wrath of the "so-called" hydrogen bomb. Safety is a question that lurks in everyone's mind; hydrogen is equated with danger. However, if we take a closer look at hydrogen's properties, its many beneficial uses throughout history and in our modern day lives, the tarnished reputation could very well be replaced with a new, positive stature.

Throughout the universe, hydrogen atoms are constantly being smashed with other hydrogen atoms under extreme gravitational force. This pressure is so great that for every four hydrogen nuclei fused together, a single helium nucleus is formed. The fusion of these elements creates energy that our eyes perceive as light. In the heavens, these lights are called stars, and the most brilliant of these, mankind has named the "sun." Every second, 700 million tons of hydrogen are converted to helium ashes to keep the sun shining.

Stars cluster to form galaxies such as our Milky Way. Moving rapidly through the outer regions of the Milky Way are high-velocity clouds—flashy and mysterious clumps of hydrogen, up to 10 million times the mass of the sun and 10,000 light years across.

Hydrogen, the most abundant element in the cosmos, is the key to generating the most vital substance on earth: water. Life on earth began in water and cannot exist without it. Living cells are made up of 70 to 95 percent water and it covers approximately three-quarters of the earth's surface. The word "hydrogen" derives from the Greek words, "hydro" which means water and "genes" which means forming.

Scientists describe certain "laws" of nature that serve as key roles in the explanation of theories of origin. Concepts such as the conservation laws of total energy, linear momentum, and angular momentum are some examples. Using hydrogen as the building block, nature applies these laws and this leads to the creation of other elements and compounds, which, in turn, bond and grow together to form chunks of matter such as asteroids and comets. Those entities find, and orbit a mother star we call planets or moons. The most familiar of these planets to us mankind has named "earth."

Few biological processes are as essential to life as the complex "molecular origami" known as protein folding. Proteins begin in cells as one-dimensional strings. Within a fraction of a second, they fold into their divinely programmed 3-D shapes. As exquisitely crafted molecular ideograms, they are instantly ready to do nature's work—everything from digesting food to making hormones. The proteins are thus the single, most versatile, and widely used compounds in animal bodies like our own. A protein is made up of carbon, oxygen and nitrogen atoms glued together.

The glue is hydrogen.

Here on earth every living creature is ultimately dependent upon plant life. Plants are the only organisms that can actually fabricate their own food, and they do this through a process known as "photosynthesis." When sunlight or artificial light hits a plant's leaves and carbon dioxide is absorbed from the air, sugars, starch, fats and proteins are produced, thus creating a food source for animals. Hydrogen is absorbed by the plant from water and then attaches itself to carbon atoms and "reduction" takes place—meaning that the hydrogen reduces the carbon dioxide by splitting off the oxygen molecules. The plant then releases this oxygen into the atmosphere, thereby supplying us with what we breathe!

Clearly, hydrogen is the lifeblood of God's Universe.

Hydrogen is both simple and complex. If we could take an "Alice in Wonderland" trip and step through the looking glass into the world of atoms and molecules, we would see the simple makeup of hydrogen: one proton with one electron swirling about it. Another world deeper, and we would find ourselves swimming in a complex "alphabet soup" of neutrinos, gluons, bosons, "up" quarks and "down" quarks. Imagine that! Even hydrogen has its ups and downs. And now physicists have found the elusive pentaquark, leading to more understanding of sub-atomic interactions.

In nature, hydrogen and electricity are the best of buddies. Take away the proton and hydrogen becomes electricity. Both of them are energy carriers. Electrolysis of water, the process of using electricity to split the water molecules, produces hydrogen and oxygen. Putting the hydrogen and oxygen back together again, using a device called a "fuel cell" produces electricity and water. How perfectly efficient can you get!

In spite of the fact that hydrogen is the most abundant element in the Universe, it is not found lingering around in the atmosphere in any significant quantity by itself. In fact any free hydrogen released into the atmosphere wiggles its way past the oxygen and nitrogen to the upper atmosphere and goes off into the cosmos where it came from. Some claim the hydrogen will link up with ozone in the stratosphere to form water and free oxygen. Not obtainable directly from the atmosphere, hydrogen has to be gleaned from other sources. It is "locked up" in water, so to speak, and held captive in many compounds such as coal and natural gas. With a certain amount of energy, however, the hydrogen can be extracted and put to use in many beneficial ways.

Isolated and identified more than a century ago by English physicist and chemist, Henry Cavendish, and later named by French scientist Antoine Lavoisier, hydrogen has found its way into industry's processes. It is used in the manufacture of glass, chemicals, pharmaceuticals, fertilizers, adhesives, surfactants, computer chips and rocket fuel.

As a fuel, it burns with a very clean flame. This is important in its use for the production of fiber optics and high quality quartz.

To the present day, the dominant world fuel source has been heavy crude oil. The burning of this oil to create energy releases high amounts of sulfur and nitrogen oxides creating air pollution that damages health and poisons the environment in countless ways. In refining, hydrogen comes to our aid when it is used to "hydrogenate" the sulfur and nitrogen compounds in the fuel oil. This decreases the amount of the toxic compounds when the fuel is burned, and thereby helps to reduce the pollutants.

Also in the area of energy production, hydrogen is needed and used in advanced nuclear reactors to scavenge the troublesome trace amounts of oxygen that interfere with the process. With its low level of viscosity, it can also reduce friction in the reactor's power generation armature, or rotating coil, hence reducing the cooling loads.

In 1983, US President Ronald Reagan announced his

Strategic Defense Initiative, (also known as "Star Wars"), a program whose concept was to create a defense system capable of intercepting and destroying enemy ballistic missiles using space-based lasers. Although the program has undergone changes since the cold-war era, research and development of the technology continues, and hydrogen still plays a key role. Although there are many types of lasers made from many different materials, these space-based lasers require a very high-energy property. Hydrogen and fluorine are combined to produce hydrogen fluoride, a substance that promotes discharge of high-powered bursts of infrared radiation capable of shattering its intended target.

Hydrogen comes in handy in more subtle applications too. When directly combined with nitrogen (at high temperatures assisted by a catalyst), it becomes ammonia, whose major use is as a fertilizer. It is also used to formulate the "hydroxyls" now used in cosmetic applications to diminish age spots, scars and wrinkles.

One of the most astonishing hydrogen mixtures, "hydrogen peroxide", when used in low concentrations, serves as an antiseptic or as a hair-bleaching agent. Scientists have found it is involved in virtually all of life's vital processes. It stimulates the immune system, helps your body fight off viruses, parasites and bacteria. It also regulates hormones and is involved in the production of energy in the body's cells. That's just a few of the amazing things it does. Also amazing is that in a highly concentrated form, hydrogen peroxide can be used as a rocket fuel!

The invention of the hydrogen atomic clock has led to its use to track space probes. It only loses a second in 300 million years!

In a medical application, when a physician suspects that

someone may have lactose intolerance, hydrogen comes in handy as a diagnostic tool. A "hydrogen breath test" is performed by giving the patient a lactose-laden drink and then analyzing the levels of hydrogen in his or her breath at specific intervals. Normally, only trace amounts of hydrogen can be detected in the breath, but, if raised levels are discovered, this may indicate that a person's system is not properly digesting lactose and the result is that hydrogen, along with other gases, are produced and released when the breath is exhaled.

Speaking of medicine, it was the experiments with hydrogen in the 1930's that led to the development of a magnetic resonance method to study the nucleus of the hydrogen atom and its sister deuterium. This important science was used to develop the magnetic resonance imaging (MRI) machine used as a diagnostic tool today. The MRI actually provokes the hydrogen atoms in the human body to emit signals that can be analyzed and assembled into images. The images provide the physician detailed information about the physical condition of the patient.

Another amazing hydrogen fact exists in connection with a microorganism called methanogen. They eat hydrogen, breathe carbon dioxide and belch methane. And they form the root of an ecosystem unlike any known on earth. This tiny organism lives in complete darkness 660 feet under the surface of Idaho. Methanogens could represent the sort of life to look for on other planets.

From high above in our earth's atmosphere to the depths of our seas, the beneficial applications of hydrogen are abundant. The phaseout of CFC refrigerants, in view of their destructive effect on our ozone layer, resulted in the introduction of the hydrogen compound, HCF, as an acceptable near term refrigerant replacement. The US Navy has been testing a hydrogen/oxygen mix as a new breathing "air" for its deep-sea divers. For extreme depths, the hydrogen is substituted for the commonly used helium. This reduces the chance of the diver contracting the "bends."

The simplicity of the hydrogen atom has enabled scientists to unravel some of the mysteries of nature and the cosmos. The discovery that hydrogen deep in space has its own radio signature, at a constant wavelength of 21 centimeters, opened up the exciting field of radio astronomy. As a result, the simplest amino acid was discovered in space, the building block of life. Shifts in the hydrogen wavelength also give clues to astronomers about the motion of galaxies.

Many common household products are processed with hydrogen, including plastic milk containers, garbage bags, Vitamins A and C, toothpaste, soap and lipstick. Automobile fuel injectors and spark plugs, as well as nails and wire in a house are just a few examples of products fabricated by annealing, sintering or brazing of metal; all processes employing hydrogen.

Hydrogen is, of course, used as a reducing agent in the manufacture of computer chips. Now researchers are looking at using what is called supercritical carbon dioxide to help in making the chips. The carbon dioxide allows metallic compounds to be poured into tight nooks and crannies of trenches etched into the chip silicon to form wires. But when hydrogen gas is added, the metallic compounds release their loads onto the silicon surface to create high quality interconnects thinner than 100 nanometers. Now what is a nanometer? Well, it is a unit of measure equaling a billionth of a meter. Ok, a human hair is 10,000 nanometers across, a common virus is 100 nanometers across and in case you really need to know this, 10 hydrogen atoms lined up end to end is one nanometer.

Ladies, visualize this: at your favorite major cosmetic company, out in the back of the building is a small storage tank. Routinely, an eighteen-wheeler tanker truck pulls up and off-loads a few hundred gallons of liquid hydrogen into the tank. As needed, the liquid is converted to a gas and fed to the process equipment in the building to make your favorite cosmetics.

Courtesy Air Products and Chemicals

Guys, ponder this: during the commercial, as you are watching the Rams take on the 49ers on the wide screen television, think of all the electronics, including your remote. Yes, hydrogen also played a role, and pay attention to the butter in that popcorn.

Certain foods, such as margarine, salad dressing, and peanut butter benefit from a longer shelf life when they are hydrogen-processed or "hydrogenated."

If all this is beginning to give you a headache, you could go take an aspirin, which is, yes you guessed it, also made with the help of hydrogen!

* * *

As a gas, hydrogen has some very interesting characteristics. It is the lightest (but not the smallest) of all molecules and at room temperature it's very buoyant and diffuses through air much more rapidly than other gases. Like methane, it is colorless, odorless, tasteless and nontoxic. Flammable in air, it can be ignited with a relatively small amount of energy. The lowest is at "stoichiometric" which is the optimum ratio of fuel and air needed for proper combustion in, for example, an automobile engine. It also burns with a comparatively faster flame speed if its concentration is not very lean or very rich. With a higher ignition temperature than common fuels, hydrogen also burns with a nearly invisible flame in daylight. These flames emit a low level of thermal radiation, thus reducing secondary ignitions and burns.

When looking at all these facts, hydrogen appears to have qualities that make its use more desirable, from the standpoint of safety, than those of other fuels. Its lower limit of flammability is not much different from that of other fuel gases. Moreover, its high characteristic diffusivity increases its tendency to dilute to below flammability levels. Hydrogen's buoyancy causes it to typically burn upward, thus minimizing secondary effects in a hydrogen fire.

I have often encountered armchair engineers who are quick to point out the dangers of hydrogen because of its low ignition energy and wide flammability range. In practice, the concern is focused on the lower flammability limit, as this is most probable with a potential leak. The problem here is that the low ignition energy "concern" is at the ideal fuel/air ratio. At the lean end of the hydrogen/air flammable mix, or the lower flammability limit, the required ignition energy is the same as for natural gas, which has been used extensively for years in homes. In addition, most common sources of ignition are sufficient to ignite gasoline and other fuels. An experiment (and please do NOT attempt this!) is to put a lighted cigarette in a flammable mix of hydrogen and air. The thermal energy is too low, so, nothing happens. But, what do you think could happen should you foolishly decide to keep that burning cigarette between your lips while filling up your tank at you local gas station? If you're not sure how to answer that, let the word "KABOOM" be a hint!

The public has come to accept the risks of using the conventional carbon-based fuels and electrical conveniences. Pumping gasoline, lighting a propane barbecue, and plugging in electrical appliances are all commonplace events that can and do result in accidents, but the risk has been accepted. In view of this, it is important to assess hydrogen on a comparative basis, realizing that it must also be handled with respect and appropriate safeguards.

Though probably not common knowledge, for the past 50 years, gaseous hydrogen has been used in large quantities as a feedstock. Worldwide, the annual consumption of hydrogen is about 400 billion cubic meters. Almost all of it is used in a "captive" state, that is, it's consumed on site at the refinery or chemical plant. Hydrogen is used to make gasoline. Nevertheless, a safe and reliable hydrogen distribution network has been developed over the years, consisting of liquid hydrogen delivery trucks, gaseous hydrogen tube trailers, and dedicated gaseous hydrogen pipelines.

Annually in the US about, 40,000 shipments are made to

over 1,000 locations. In many cases, several locations can be serviced with one tanker load. Liquid hydrogen is being carried safely on US highways at a rate of over 100 million gallons per year with very few mishaps. Prior to 1960, tankers were designed with a 7,000-gallon capacity. The tankers currently being built will hold 17,000 gallons, limited by DOT over-the-road dimensional and weight criteria. I have estimated that in the last 30 years the hydrogen industrial tankers have logged over three billion miles with an amazing safety record. Railway transportation has also been used to ship liquid hydrogen from coast to coast.

Hydrogen also has a long history of use in both homes and factories as a fuel. In the 19th century, "coal gas", a mixture of hydrogen, methane and carbon monoxide was used extensively in Great Britain for lighting. In the US, prior to World War II, "town gas", a 50/50 mixture of hydrogen and carbon monoxide made by gasifying coal, was used by millions of Americans to cook food, light lamps, and heat water and homes.

Today, in many countries, the major use of hydrogen as a fuel is in the space programs and engine research and development projects. Liquid hydrogen is used as a rocket engine fuel and as an on-board fuel cell feedstock to provide electricity and drinking water for the astronauts, cosmonauts and other nauts. These applications have been instrumental in developing a robust and safe production and delivery system for hydrogen. Excellent safety records have been established in handling large quantities of hydrogen, primarily due to strict adherence to standard practices and operating procedures, as well as effective training of personnel.

As we humans search the heavens new and exciting things are being found. The Hubble space telescope sends us pictures of giant hydrogen gas clouds in the process of making the ingredients for new planets. If the universe has too much hydrogen it will contract, but if the supply is at the right balance the universe will expand forever.

On very large planets and stars, the hydrogen is under extreme pressure. This is where metallic hydrogen is produced. If we can eventually accomplish this on earth via a high-pressure machine, it would give birth to a new branch of physics and revolutionize our concept and usage of energy as we now know it.

Somewhere, out there, may also be a universe of antimatter, which would conceivably contain anti-hydrogen. Additionally, there is the realm of "dark matter" and "missing matter," cosmologists suggest make up for apparent discrepancies in the mass balance of the universe. Dark matter does not give off light, therefore a visible light telescope cannot detect it. However, other types of sensors sent into space suggest the existence of this matter. Recent works indicate the missing matter as hydrogen ions. Could the dark matter be yet another "form" of hydrogen or perhaps be influenced by it? There are still so many intriguing questions to be posed and whole new worlds of knowledge that remain to be explored.

Let's now take a moment to revisit and address the subject of hydrogen's "beastly" reputation in its role with the hydrogen bomb. The branding of this horrific weapon of mass destruction as a "hydrogen" bomb is in fact a misconstruing of the elements and chain of events that take place. The hydrogen bomb is not really a "hydrogen" device in the true sense of the word. To achieve explosion, the process requires the fusing of a rare isotope of hydrogen called tritium (typically produced by bombarding lithium with neutrons). Furthermore, the fusion reaction requires extreme pressure and temperature conditions, and this can only be accomplished via the atomic process of fissioning uranium or plutonium isotopes. This misnomer is somewhat akin to calling a lump of graphite a diamond since they are both forms of carbon. While on a visit to the Department of Energy facilities at Oak Ridge, Tennessee, I saw the B-83 "hydrogen" bomb, a thermonuclear device. Man! It is small enough to sit on my office desk!

I spoke of tritium. The total amount on earth in the natural state is about two pounds, mostly in the ocean. Study by W.F.Libby indicates that tritium (radiohydrogen) may be an excellent tracer (like carbon 14 dating) for studying the movements of air and moisture over the planet.

And there you have it, some basics about hydrogen. Next, we look at other aspects of hydrogen and a number of activities going on to implement it as the future fuel as well as an energy carrier along with electricity.

Chapter 16

Toward The Future

- *Technology tells us what we can do.*
- *Economics tells us what we should do.*
- *Politics tells us what we will do.*

Before looking to the future I would like to pause and share a statement made in 1875 just as gasoline coupled with the "horseless carriage" concept was entering the marketplace. It is a summary of a report of the Congressional Horseless Carriage Committee. It is quoted in the original format.

"A new source of power, which comes from a distillate of kerosene called gasoline, has been produced by a Boston engineer. Instead of burning the fuel under a boiler, it is exploded inside the cylinder of the engine. This so-called internal combustion engine may be used under certain conditions to supplement steam engines. Experiments are underway to use an engine to propel a vehicle.

This discovery begins a new era in the history of civilization. It may someday prove to be more revolutionary in the development of human society than the invention of the wheel, the use of metals, or the steam engine. Never in history has society been confronted with power so full of potential danger and at the same time so full of promise for the future of man for the peace of the world.

The dangers are obvious. Stores of gasoline in the hands of the people interested primarily in profit would constitute a fire and explosive hazard of the first rank. Horseless carriages propelled by gasoline engines might attain speeds of 14 or even 20 miles per hour. The menace to our people of vehicles of this type hurtling through our streets and along our roads poisoning our atmosphere would call for prompt legislative action even if the military and economic implications were not so overwhelming.

The Secretary of War has testified before us and has pointed out the destructive effects of the use of such vehicles in battle. A few of them with a small cannon mounted behind a steel shield could decimate infantry, break up a cavalry charge, and even seriously threaten the efficacy of field artillery by lightning-like flank attacks.

Furthermore, our supplies of petroleum, from which gasoline is extracted only in limited quantities, make it imperative that the defense forces should have first call on the limited supply.

Furthermore, the cost of producing it is beyond the financial capacity of private industry, yet the safety of the nation demands that an adequate supply should be produced.

In addition, the development of this new power may displace the use of horses, which would wreck our agriculture.

We therefore earnestly recommend that Congress set up a Horseless Carriage Commission which will have complete control over all sources of gasoline and similar explosive elements and all activities connected with their development and use in the United States.

These measures may seem drastic and far-reaching but the discovery with which we are dealing involves forces of nature too dangerous to fit into our usual concepts."

Hopefully the public will not characterize hydrogen, to be used as an automotive fuel, in the same manner; or for that matter, in any transportation scheme.

Hydrogen has been called the perfect fuel and energy carrier by hydrogen, energy and environmental interests. Its major reserve on earth (water) is inexhaustible. The by-products of its use are heat and water. The use of hydrogen is compatible with nature, rather than intrusive. We simply will never run out of hydrogen.

The greatest promise for a renewable energy future is held within the two energy currencies, namely, hydrogen and electricity. Electricity is clean and fast, but cannot be effectively stored. Hydrogen can be readily stored and transported. Hydrogen can make electricity, and electricity can make hydrogen. Together, they create an energy loop that is completely renewable and harmless to the environment. The future challenge is of course to see that the origin of hydrogen or its electrical counterpart is not traceable back to a carbon based fuel.

Today the use of hydrogen is as varied as the global marketplace. The properties of hydrogen are well known to a variety of producers of consumer goods and services, and understanding the special properties of hydrogen is necessary for its safe use.

In the near term ahead, the transition years, hydrogen produced from conventional methods may be needed to extend the useful life of petroleum, and perhaps coal and natural gas. During this period, niche applications will be implemented to progressively allow the entry of renewable energy, hydrogen and related technologies.

Beyond the transition years, hydrogen produced from wind and solar resources will be the ultimate, abundant, renewable-based energy form. Growing concerns about global climate change, fostered by fossil fuel emissions, promise to expand hydrogen use from its familiar role in space to the pollution-free fuel and energy carrier of ordinary earthbound uses like cooking and transportation. Part of the difficulty in bringing hydrogen to its full commercial potential is the public's perception that hydrogen is extraordinarily dangerous, based on some stereotyped misunderstandings of certain events.

Nuclear energy has the same misunderstanding. It is ideal to produce the electrical energy we need as well as making hydrogen (using the high temperatures to break down water) to move energy to locations where it is needed as a fuel. No one was injured or died as a result of Three Mile Island. A plant like Chernobyl would never pass US specifications. The plants are not nuclear bombs. No greenhouse gases, no bad pollutants like sulfur dioxide, nitrogen oxide or carbon dioxide. Waste? Yes but newer reactors can produce over 100 times as much energy than the older designs with a corresponding decrease in the amount of waste produced. Looking for something perfect? No way, even the "renewable energy" wind turbines producing electrical power in California kill birds.

Hydrogen, like all fuels, and hydrogen as an energy carrier like electricity, by their nature, can be dangerous. Hydrogen safety continues to be of utmost importance, not only to those working routinely with hydrogen, but to the general public as well. Hydrogen handling has had an excellent safety record. This is due to the use of proper safety precautions, familiarization with not only the properties of hydrogen in the form in which it is (gaseous or liquid), but familiarization with, and application of, related rules, regulations and standards established through years of experience and research.

Industry has consistently demonstrated its ability to safely produce, ship and handle hydrogen as a gas as well as in liquid form. NASA's experience with the safe use of both gaseous and liquid hydrogen over many decades continues to prove that experience using hydrogen can lead to impressive applications that will favorably impact our future economy and environment. The key factors in NASA's successful approach to hydrogen safety are the applications of proper engineering practices to the design of equipment and facilities, integration of a safety hazard analysis program into every process phase, and development of standard operating procedures. Orientation to the properties and nature of hydrogen behavior are essential.

As we have learned, hydrogen has properties that make it unique from a safety standpoint, like its lighter than air property and high diffusion rate. Materials compatibility is an important factor in systems design. Research and testing projects continue throughout industrial, academic and government institutions to improve the safety of using hydrogen. These include improved and reliable detection techniques.

The public has come to accept the risks involved in personally using the conventional carbon based fuels and electrical conveniences. It is important then to assess hydrogen on a comparative basis. Hydrogen is an unknown to most of the public in terms of its usefulness, but is characterized by a negative stigma. This enhances the need to demonstrate and prove that handling and storing hydrogen involves no greater risk than carbon-based fuels. Comparative tests and studies have concluded that using hydrogen in some aspects is a lesser risk than conventional fuels. What these assessments provide is the identification of where to focus further research. The automotive, fuel supplier and home energy industries over the decades have engineered their products such that they can be used at a low or acceptable risk. The challenge is to *communicate* that hydrogen can also be used in these industries with a low or acceptable risk.

The University of Miami has conducted many experiments to demonstrate that gasoline is perhaps just as bad as methane or hydrogen. When hydrogen was first considered as a fuel for aircraft the "Skunk Works" at Burbank did much testing. The following is taken from John Sloop's book regarding those tests. *(Liquid Hydrogen as a Propulsion Fuel, 1945-1959, NASA, 1978).*

"Tests were devised in which tanks containing liquid hydrogen under pressure were ruptured. In many cases, the hydrogen quickly escaped without ignition. The experimenters then provided a rocket squib (a small powder charge) to ignite the escaping hydrogen. The resulting fireball quickly dissipated because of the rapid flame speed of hydrogen and its low density. Containers of hydrogen and gasoline were placed side-by-side and ruptured. When the hydrogen can was ruptured and ignited, the flame quickly dissipated; but when the same thing was done with gasoline the flame stayed near the container and did much more damage. The gasoline fire was an order of magnitude more severe than the hydrogen fire. The experimenters tried to induce hydrogen to explode, with limited success. In 61 attempts, only two explosions occurred and in both, they had to mix oxygen with the hydrogen."

A national newspaper reports on an accident with a car that slammed into a tanker truck carrying gasoline just outside a gas station in East Islip, New York. It triggered an explosion that shook houses several blocks away and shot flames more than 100 feet in the air. The driver of the car died. The article was on page 15 of the *New York Times*. Had hydrogen been involved it would have been on page one, I assure you. One reads about this kind of thing a lot, also the fires that break out while people are filling their car with gasoline. Now you see labels on the gasoline dispensers, warning about static electricity and the precautions one should take.

Yes, over the years there have been accidents involving hydrogen, but nowhere near what we have experienced with other hazardous commodities. In some cases, hydrogen may have been involved, but not the actual cause. I do not mean to take these events lightly, as hydrogen can be a problem if not properly dealt with.

I can compare apples with apples. A hydrogen supplier showed me photos of the incident where a car slammed into the side of a 13,000-gallon liquid hydrogen truck tanker. The car's gasoline tank explodes, destroying the car and killing the driver, causing fire damage to the tanker. Not a drop of hydrogen was lost.

Organizations such as the American Hydrogen Association and outreach projects sponsored by the government, industry and academic institutions will provide the mechanism to communicate the attributes of hydrogen to the general public and to help alleviate their fears.

The National Hydrogen Association, using the experience base of the hydrogen industry as well as academic institutions, hydrogen technological industries and the government, support the preparation of hydrogen publications, such as the brochure, "Handling Hydrogen Safely."

Although millions of pounds of hydrogen are used daily across the country some of the energy and transportation fueling concepts under consideration, when implemented, will greatly increase the use of hydrogen. New concepts will require the development of related safety designs, practices and rules. For example, the use of fuel cells in the automotive sector or on site hydrogen generators will require that appropriate controls, codes and standards be developed. This effort is underway.

The use of cryogenic hydrogen in the ground transportation sector is under serious consideration by many countries. Hydrogen has the highest combustion energy per pound relative to other fuels, meaning hydrogen is more efficient on a weight basis than fuels currently used. This density-energy factor makes it an attractive aircraft fuel. There have been limited projects using the cryogenic state of hydrogen in ground as well as air transport, (maybe a Boeing 7H7 someday). These activities further the need to develop related safety equipment designs, rules and standards.

Over the years, much effort has gone into the preparation and publication of guidelines and requirements for hydrogen systems and equipment. In the United States, the National Fire Protection Association publishes guidelines for storage systems. The Department of Transportation regulates the distribution of hydrogen over the nation's roads. Associations like the American National Standards Institute and the American Society of Mechanical Engineers publish standards for components used in hydrogen equipment. The Compressed Gas Association sets standards for many gases including hydrogen, and their publications cover gas production, handling and use.

However, with the consideration of new applications of hydrogen it becomes necessary to expand the codes and standards library. The National Hydrogen Association, with assistance from the Department of Energy, periodically hosts workshops addressing the development of hydrogen codes and standards.

With the international movement of implementing hydrogen as a fuel and energy medium the International Standards Organization (ISO), as noted earlier, created a hydrogen technologies committee (ISO TC 197). This committee, with its working groups, is in the process of identifying and developing the necessary standards to assure the uniformity of hydrogen component and system designs, specifications and guidelines around the world. Some standards have already been published with many others now in draft form.

A recent publication, "The Sourcebook for Hydrogen Applications" was funded by the National Resources Canada and the US Department of Energy and sponsored jointly by the Canadian Hydrogen Association and the National Hydrogen Association. The Hydrogen Research Institute of Canada and the National Renewable Energy Laboratory of the US oversaw its preparation. There were ten of us that worked together to prepare this document.

The Sourcebook is a compilation of prevailing practices and applicable codes, standards, guidelines, and regulations for the safe use of hydrogen. It provides an introductory reference document that outlines key safety considerations for designing, building, and using hydrogen as a fuel in nonindustrial applications.

The recognition and adoption of uniform practices is paramount to assure adequate hydrogen safety operations. The standards set by national and international organizations are high. It is industry's long-standing commitment to these high standards that enables hydrogen to be safely handled and used today, and gives the needed experience and knowledge for the future.

There is concern with the pace of codes and standards publications keeping up with the technologies. Also, there is concern by the US members of various working groups on international influence over the US inputs. This simply is the problem of inadequate support by US interests in sponsoring the necessary membership participation. I do not put this at the fault of the sponsoring companies or organizations, but the fact is the experts are spread too thin and travel budgets are limited. Also, we need more industry participation.

With unfamiliar devices entering the marketplace such as fuel cells and reformers under the hood, exotic storage tanks in the trunk, gas detectors at various vehicular locations, there is a need for not only public awareness but also education and involvement of the rule makers.

For the success of any new hydrogen technology project there is what one may call the Cardinal Rule. That is, the total involvement of the project's corporate internal organizations and the early involvement of local building officials, fire marshals, insurance agents, permitting agents and the like. The hydrogen supplier must participate as well.

The public must be educated that hydrogen as a new fuel to the community will have a significantly new characteristic. Unlike the visibility and smell of gasoline and the odor of natural gas or propane, hydrogen will be odorless and colorless. However with the rapid development of hydrogen specific detection devices and systems, safety of this new fuel will actually be enhanced. The basic problem with the historical odorization of natural gas is that it does not render an assessment of the real situation in the event of a leak. One knows there is a problem, but then the questions become exactly where, how much, and is a flammable situation really at hand. The new detection technologies provide disciplined safety, situational awareness and verifiable tiered response—something odorants cannot do. The role of any odorant might be as a means of a first alert. But, remember, there needs to be a human nose nearby, and one that works! The olfactory system could overload and mask the smell. This happens often in the bottom of a ship where there may be sulfide related fumes and the sailors become unaware of the impending danger of asphyxiation *and die.*

The implementation of new sensor/detection technologies should not be of concern to the public because, in the home, we already have smoke, carbon monoxide, and motion detectors. The automobile is full of warning devices and other information sensors.

I have a little story for you. I asked my wife what she would do if she entered the kitchen and smelled natural gas, verifying that the "knobs" were in the off position. Aside from throwing open some windows, she said she would go to the neighbors and call 911. Okay, but if the range operated on hydrogen and a red light came on, indicating that the main fuel line valve was automatically shutoff, what then?

"I would wait until you came home to fix the problem," was her reply.

In our quest to meet the energy needs of the future and the continuance of reliance on energy sources having limited supply, the subject of human safety is a common denominator to all. Typically, the subject of safety has to do with a particular fuels' safety from say, a fire or an explosion. That is, it is vital to protect people from the immediate threat of danger, harm, or loss. But let us take that threat of danger, harm, or loss to the less obvious aspect of the day- to-day living environment. Coal-fired power plants releasing toxic mercury that finds its way to fish that we eat; Coal dust, diesel fumes, oil spills, carbon here—carbon there. Cancer, respiratory problems, ailments here—ailments there. We must establish a clean environment for the safety of humans and other precious life forms on our mother-earth spaceship. One should also consider our safety as may be influenced by the consequences of actions of the petroleum czars. The safety of using hydrogen must be assessed. All of hydrogen's attributes must be considered and the relationship it can clearly have versus our other energy and fuel options. We humans started with wood as a fuel source. It is 90% carbon; then we learned to burn coal at 62% carbon; oil at 35%; then natural gas at 20%; and finally, hydrogen … no carbon.

* * *

Yes, I still go to the Twins for fly-fishing. But now the road has improved to allow more traffic. The occasional whiff of diesel fumes is evident as I make a cast,

trying in vain to remember I went there to get away from the world with its problems—you know a little piece of heaven and tranquility. The air was pure and clean. I could take a drinking cup and dip it into the nice cool water and not be concerned about it being safe. Not so today.

I use to love to walk on the beach in Satellite Beach, Florida where I once lived in a condo. Close to HWY A1A, the ocean view was breathtaking in more than one way, as automotive exhaust from passing cars fills the air. And then oil droplets in the sand stick to your bare feet, evidence of ships at sea dumping their bilge water, contaminated with crude oil.

Dad's concern about the percentage of oxygen in the air continued to intrigue me. While I was in charge of propellants and life support at NASA, I was made aware of the difficulties of making liquid air to use in life support equipment. The problem was making sure that the mix had 20 % oxygen mixed with 80% nitrogen, but if stored over time, the relative percent of oxygen went up as some of the liquid nitrogen turned to gas and vented off. As a rule of thumb, when the mix approached 25%, the product would be discarded. The problem was the enriched oxygen became incompatible with certain materials rendering them highly reactive and of course the increased hazard of flammability.

According to scientists like J. Lovelock, if the atmospheric oxygen content rose to 22%, the ability of the air to support combustion would increase to 70%. At 25 % oxygen, any ignition source would trigger a fire that would engulf the earth and destroy all living things. And of course, as the percent drops below 19.5%, creatures may start having problems with breathing. At 16% you're a gonner. I have read that in the days of the dinosaurs, the oxygen level may have been on the high side, leading to many fires.

In recent work scientists are finding that methane from bacterial fermentation of microorganisms actually is the basis of a process to regulate the atmospheric oxygen and maintain the 21% balance … the answer to Dad's question.

You may wonder why I spend time discussing oxygen in a "hydrogen" book.

Mother Nature is beautiful, isn't it, but mankind continues to do things that could mess up Mother's delicate recipe. A point here is the role of hydrogen instead of the polluting petrol fuels that change our delicate air chemistry.

There is the factor of six billion people filling the world to consider, and feeling so good about it they are going to produce another two billion oxygen breathers during the balance of my lifetime. Yeah, okay, I am being sarcastic.

The propellant function at KSC involves the pumping out of the submarine bilges at dockside in Port Canaveral. This offered me the opportunity to visit below deck on some occasions. The British subs were really cramped. Then I got to go aboard the attack sub the Sea Wolf. It too was just a little claustrophobic. Then friend Randy Harris, a member of the military affairs council, made arrangements for me to go out on the USS Nebraska nuclear sub, affectionately called a "boomer."

As we got beyond the continental shelf, to my surprise, I got to sit at the controls. Here I was at the wheel of a machine 560 feet long, 42 feet in diameter and weighing in at over 18,000 tons. I was surprised at the quick response of the control. I could monitor the depth gauge as I dived to 800 feet, then leveled out. What a feeling. Here I was actually steering a machine that had enough missile power to wipe out 240 cities the size of Chicago. That is, ten warheads on each of the 24 missiles on board, each warhead can be programmed for a target, and each having the firepower of many times the bomb we dropped on Hiroshima.

Sweat breaks out on my forehead as I wonder how many of these "boats" we have. Amazingly, there was enough fuel on board to stay under for over 20 years! Crew time and food are the constraints requiring submariners to go to port every few months.

The crew makes on-board breathing oxygen from seawater. Sea salt is taken out of the water then an electrolyzer splits the water into oxygen and

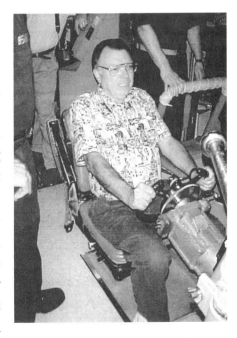

279

hydrogen. Of course I had to ask what they did with the hydrogen. It is vented overboard.

Then of course there are the torpedoes. You remember seeing ships being blown up in WW ll by subs. Well now the action is different. The target ship is not blown up. The torpedo is sent by computer to the underside of the ship and detonated. The rapid displacement of water under the keel creates a void. The water is no longer holding the ship afloat (in the center) so the ship breaks in half!

* * *

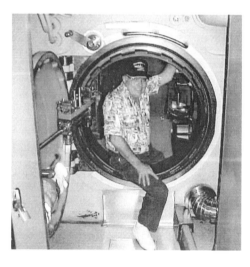

Hydrogen interests continue to provide me the opportunity to get involved with a number of events and to meet people. Actor Dennis Weaver is an advocate of hydrogen, Jay Leno the car buff likes the idea, and then I met Chauncey Starr, President Emeritus of EPRI (Electrical Power Research Institute). He has this neat idea of the Continental Super Grid, based on hydrogen-cooled superconductor and nuclear power. It is a concept that would provide an underground "cable" to supply both electricity as well as hydrogen through a grid network throughout the US. Maybe something for the 22nd century? Dennis Weaver has an organization called Institute of Ecolonomics. His newsletter usually has something about hydrogen.

Automaker BMW brings me on board occasionally to

Dennis Weaver

address hydrogen related issues in their grand plan with liquid hydrogen fueled cars. Of all concepts including automotive fuel cell ideas, I still think the BMW is the most superb. This is probably because I am an old internal combustion engine (ICE) advocate. I probably made a mistake one time criticizing the Department of Energy for discontinuing ICE research and jumping on board with all the furor of the fuel cell. You may not know this but the fuel cell car is really an electric car. The batteries (of the typical electric car) are replaced with a fuel cell that provides electricity to operate the electric drive motors at the wheels or drive train. But the fuel cell needs hydrogen to operate, so you are led to believe it is a "hydrogen fueled" car. The hydrogen could come from reforming a chemical stored on-board like methanol. In the space business we called the supply of hydrogen to the fuel cell a *reactant*. The hydrogen to the space vehicle engines was, of course, the fuel.

For me, I view the fuel cell-powered "family" car as a

Jay Leno

novelty for the rich and famous for some time to come. The very high quality of hydrogen fuel required may be much more expensive than that needed for a hydrogen fueled ICE. Also, I believe a revolutionary advance in technology will be required, not the evolutionary change we experienced with the petrol economy. Clearly the fuel cell for portable, large mobile machines, and stationary power applications has great near-term promise. The BMW hydrogen car actually has a small fuel cell in the trunk to provide electrical power. You can sit in a parking lot with the engine off and still run the air conditioning.

The inherent venting of the liquid hydrogen fuel tank is an issue where BMW is making good progress. The fuel tank design allows surrounding air to be drawn in, then liquefied using the exit hydrogen energy, but stored in a surrounding cooling jacket and thus acts to provide further refrigeration to keep the hydrogen from venting. So far a vehicle can sit for 12 days before evaporation loss starts to occur, but extending this timeframe is in the works. I will not be surprised if BMW will improve the overall efficiency of their concept.

BMW also has perfected a really neat fueling dispenser. It can fill the car's fuel tank in about three minutes, all automatically, without getting out of the car, and a hell of a lot safer than dispensing gasoline at a dispenser.

While under agreement with BMW, I worked with Linda Gronlund, J.D. She was an inspiring technologist of hydrogen. We started a project to design and build the first over-the-road mobile hydrogen fueling station to be employed in the US. With my background of hydrogen mobile equipment design and her connections within BMW for technical assistance, we began a small, yet strong teaming arrangement within BMW. We were well into conceptualizing a design concept. Then on September the 12th 2001, I was sitting on the pool patio with my wife reading the newspaper about the tragic events of 9/11. I noticed the name. I went to my office to get Linda's business card to see if the last name was the same. It was. I went to phone BMW, busy. I went to my computer, and there was the email announcement that Linda was in the aircraft that plunged into the Pennsylvania field. Some of us have a direct family or friend connection to this tragic event, some remote, but never the less the sadness and personal hostility of it all is there.

The future potential of using hydrogen especially liquid hydrogen in all forms of transportation brings about the concern about the future availability of helium even more to light. As you recall I provided a lot of background in Chapter 3. Helium is the only element that does not freeze out at liquid hydrogen temperatures and also being nonflammable makes it the ideal purge gas.

We also don't know what the future market will be for airships and the demand for helium. In other words, the use of liquid hydrogen as a fuel depends on the future availability of helium. Helium is already used in the medical industry—MRI's, and as an oxygen enabler for pulmonary disorders like asthma.

The missile and space rocket industry, atomic energy projects, and other industrial applications have opened up interest in helium.

The US Department of Energy has commissioned research into the advanced gas-cooled reactor that would employ extreme heat to make electricity and hydrogen. The ceramic vessels of the device would be cooled by a constant flow of helium.

The hydrogen supply industry has, however, developed techniques to minimize the consumption of helium at their production plants.

I now am part of the hydrogen team at the Hydrogen Research and Applications Center in Cocoa, Florida. Under a NASA grant the team is looking at ways to better serve the hydrogen requirements of the Spaceport of the Future. Maybe I will get my chance to influence, finally, a hydrogen production plant near the launch site. Also there is the gleam in my eye, of long ago, of outfitting the Astrovan that carries the astronauts to the pad, on hydrogen fuel. I mean, what are a few gallons in a tank; they ride one into space that has a 384,000-gallon tank.

I have my own hydrogen and natural gas auto fueling station at home. My Ford Crown Victoria police cruiser is set up to take the 3,000-psig mixture of natural gas and hydrogen. With hydrogen decals ablaze on the car doors I get stopped many times by inquisitive folks and I love it! I take the time to show them the high-pressure tanks in the trunk and fueling arrangement under the hood.

"Wow! What if you are rear-ended?" They immediately ask.

I say, "God help me I don't have that 18 gallon backup gasoline tank full at the time."

Actually, the high-pressure tanks are some of the strongest parts of the car.

My station is a pretty straight -forward design. House tap water is run through a deionizer from Aqua Solutions and fed to a Proton Energy Systems hydrogen generator. The generator splits the water and hydrogen is piped to six storage tanks at 200-psig. Hydrogen is piped to the Ford storage tanks first and then topped off with high-pressure natural gas (CNG). A compressor by FuelMaker takes household natural gas and can boost it to 3,000-psig. The hydrogen tanks, piping, control panel and other components were provided by Precision Fabrication and Cleaning. A hydrogen detector is part of the assembly. A passive ventilation configuration was incorporated into the garage/attic.

* * *

I go to St. Augustine, Florida every now and then. It is the oldest city in the US and where wealthy Henry Flagler built the enormous Ponce de Leon Hotel in 1888, now functioning as Flagler College. I learned that Flagler had inventor Thomas A. Edison build an electrical power plant to provide lighting in the hallways and lobbies. Flagler had to hire a special staff trained by Edison to routinely turn the lights on and off. The people feared the new and dangerous thing called *electricity* and refused to touch the light switches on the walls! I hope we will not have that problem with hydrogen.

In the first sentence of this book I have God endorsing mankind's Big Bang theory of the origin of the universe. Now they tell me maybe we live in an ekpyrotic universe, that is, one caught in an eternal cycle of fiery birth, cooling, and rebirth. Then we have theories about what was the situation before the Big Bang. String theory and the concept of loop quantum gravity come into play. We strive for the HOW and mankind will progress on that as new machines peer into the heavens. But will we ever know WHY? Perhaps this will be the first question we will ask of our alien friends... someday. Or, maybe it is a senseless question.

Scientists are still confident that the Big Bang is a correct picture of our cosmos based on observations...so far. But general relativity allows for possible forms of energy having strange properties, strange hydrogen? Hey! I get to ponder, it's my book!

Not long ago I was back at my shop making another rocket. This one is just a model and I call it "Hyfinity." It is fueled with Newtrogen. What the devil is that, you ask? Well, the spaceship, in its motion through space, collects hydrogen and antihydrogen. Classical theory suggests that annihilation is the inevitable result if they collide head-on. But, at the CERN particle physics lab in Geneva, Switzerland, researchers suggest that it is conceivable to make a molecule made up of both atoms—that they could coexist! The possible energy of such a molecule must be fantastic. So, I coined the name *Newtrogen*, synonymous with Sir Isaac Newton's 3rd law of motion (equal magnitudes–opposite directions), or in this case, atoms of equal magnitude but opposite charge. The molecules under extreme temperature and pressure are transformed into a plasma, known as the fourth state of matter. The super hot plasma exits at a velocity approaching the speed of light, using the "ion" propulsion concept. Like I have stated, it's only a model, but it brings back the memories of Huntsville when scientist Dr. Earnst Stuhlinger was working on ion propulsion. Hey, maybe good for a science fiction story.

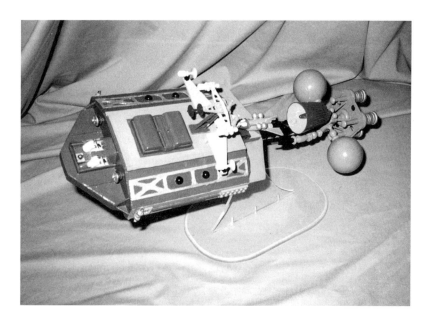

Tomorrow's hydrogen energy—the fuel and energy medium that will carry the world into its clean and sustainable energy future—will ultimately need to be produced with renewable energy technologies. Some of these technologies, such as solar and wind, have already been proven, technically.

Then there is the cost issue of implementing hydrogen fuel across the nation. We of course want to produce it such that it is not traceable to a carbon-based source, even though this is more expensive than current carbon-based hydrogen production schemes. Transportation means (cars, trains, planes, etc.) fueled by hydrogen will be more expensive, at least up front. Fueling stations and pipelines will be costly. Doesn't seem worthwhile does it? However, the price you pay at the pump or meter for hydrogen will be essentially the total cost to you. To put things in perspective, carbon based fuels at the price you pay today is not your total cost. Crank in the cost of environmental damage to air and water resources, health impacts, Persian Gulf military actions, maintaining the strategic petroleum reserve, destruction of our wildlands and wildlife sanctuaries (from oil/coal operations) and other such cost related externalities and maybe it's not so bad after all. However, I would like to quote a statement made by dear friend and colleague, Dr. David Sanborn Scott, "It seems to me that whenever reasonable and quantifiable, we should include external costs when evaluating the sustainability of development pathways. But it's unlikely. To include externalities would certainly be fair, even more important, wise. But while individuals are sometimes wise, civilizations seldom are."

Looking to the future we see many opportunities to increase the use of hydrogen. Scientists will continue to use the simple hydrogen atom as their baseline study to probe further into our understanding of the universe. What we know so far is a mysterious force called dark energy accounts for 73 percent of the entire mass-energy of the universe. Another 23 percent consists of invisible matter. That leaves us with only four percent of the universe as ordinary matter and energy! A new survey of the Milky Way detected a diffuse cloud of hydrogen gas that permeates the entire galaxy. With the fuel of stars and the preponderance of hydrogen throughout the heavens, maybe the universe is trying to tell us something? Like use it!

The environmentalists are pushing for a "green" planet—one free of human related pollution. Take a look at the pictures of the universe brought to us by the Hubble Space Telescope. The one element that shines in green (sometimes as an ionized plasma it is seen as red) is none other than … hydrogen!

The challenge for future generations is the full implementation of what can be the perfectly *safe* and *environmentally* acceptable energy medium as well as ultimately allowing us to be *free* from the shackles of petroleum.

Hydrogen, *The Freedom Element.*

Recognition

It was the support of many people that make this book what it is. The author is honored to recognize those names and identify their role.

Donna Adkins	Researcher NASA Library Kennedy Space Center, FL
Gale Allen	Microchemical Analysis Expert NASA Kennedy Space Center, FL
Hank Applegate	LZ Artifacts and History Ret. Fire Chief at Lakehurst NJ Pennsauken, NJ
Fran Ascollilo	German – English Translations Berlin, Germany
Laura Bales	Infrared Spectroscopy Expert NASA Kennedy Space Center, FL
Dr. Peter Bardehle	Zeppeliner Contacts/Translator Hamburg, Germany
Eugen Bentele	Mechanic, Hindenburg Friedrickshafen, Germany

Brett Boatright	Photo Colorization Marketing Talent Network Indian Harbor, FL
Eric Brothers	Peer Review Editor, Buoyant Flight
Cole Bryan	Failure Analysis and Materials Evaluation Expert NASA, Kennedy Space Center, FL
Robert Buchanan	Eye Witness LZ 129 Disaster Kill Devel Hills, NC
Dean Carlson	German-English Translations Melbourne, FL
Paul Christina	Editorial Consultant Kingspark, NY
David Collier	Hindenburg Artifacts and Related Data Lakewood, NJ
Jeff Cook	LZ Information and Data Lighter Than Air Society Scottsdale, AZ
Dr. Tom Crouch	National Archives Coordination Chairman, Aeronautics Department Smithsonian Institution NASM Washington, DC
Bruce Davis	Airship Data Colorado Springs, CO

Harold Dick	Airship Expert Hindenburg Construction Zeppelin-Goodyear Engineer Wichita, KS
Edith Dieckmann	German Reports Prof. Max Dieckmann Kleinmachnow, Germany
Patrick Faughnan	Thermogravimetric Analysis Expert NASA Kennedy Space Center, FL
Andy Finchum	Materials Science Expert NASA Kennedy Space Center, FL
Randy Fowler	LZ-129 Permeation Studies Hydrogen Research Division Florida Solar Energy Center Cocoa, FL
Robert Frankfort	Flame Propagation Characterization Expert NASA, Kennedy Space Center, FL
Cheryl Ganz	Airship Historian (LZ artifacts) Zeppelin Collectors Club Chicago, IL
Bob Geisler	ESD Expert Air Force Rocket Lab Edwards AFB, CA

Dr. Ray Gomph	Static Electricity Expert NASA Kennedy Space Center, FL
Debbie Guelzow	Researcher NASA Library Kennedy Space Center, FL
Senator Tom Harkin	Hydrogen/Hindenburg Research Supporter Washington, DC
Steve Huff	Electronic/Electrical Expert NASA Kennedy Space Center, FL
John Iannoceone	Eye Witness LZ-129 Disaster Lakewood, NJ
Barbara Jordan	Research of FBI Report on the Hindenburg Disaster Denver, CO
Ben Jordan	Hydrogen Advocate/ Builder of Hydrogen Vehicles Denver, CO
Dr. Kenneth Kuo	Materials Combustion Expert Director HPC Laboratory, Penn State Univ. University Park, PA
Bernard Leefer	Eye Witness LZ-129 Disaster Roosevelt, NJ

Corinna Liedtke	Interpreter (authors interviews in Germany) Zeppelin Company Friedrickshafen, Germany
Dr. Clovis Linkous	LZ-129 Permeation Experiments Hydrogen Research Division Florida Solar Energy Center Cocoa, FL
Joann Lynch	Eye Witness LZ-129 Disaster Monroe, NJ
Frank Lynch	LZ-129 Hydrogen Leak Characterization Experiments LZ-129 Electrical Arc Sensitivity Experiments President, Hydrogen Components Inc. Denver, CO
Dr. John McCarthy	Atmospheric Phenomena Expert National Atmospheric Research Center Boulder, CO
John McHale	Airplane Electrostatic Experiences United Airlines Steamboat Springs, CO
Helga Meeker	German-English Translations Titusville, FL

Dr. Wolfgang Meighorner	Zeppelin Archive Records Director, Zeppelin Museum Friedrickshafen, Germany
John Mellberg	LZ-130 Expert Ocala, FL
Dr. Claude Merrill	ESD Expert Air Force Rocket Lab Edwards AFB, CA
Karen Morris	Hindenburg Research Manuscript Preparation Merritt Island, FL
Scott Murray	Materials Science Expert NASA Kennedy Space Center, FL
Dr. Gordon Nelson	Materials Fire Characterizations Fire Science Lab Florida Institute of Technology, FL
Win Norman	Investigations FBI National Center for Analysis and Violent Crime Quantico, VA
Kent O'Grady	The Airship Heritage Trust (airship artifacts) Calgary, Canada
Kevin Pace	Airship Expert Lakehurst Historical Society Toms River, NJ

David Pfeiffer	Reference Archivist Suitland Reference Branch National Archives Washington, DC
Janet Plum	Pilot Experiences Coordination American Airlines Chicago, IL
Dr. John Provan	Airship Historian and Author Kelheim, Germany
Jim Puckett	Aircraft Operations/Regulations Expert Federal Aviation Administration Lawndale, CA
Tom Purer	Computer Analysis/Hindenburg Accident Photos NASA Kennedy Space Center, FL
Mary Ritting	Eye Witness LZ-129 Disaster West Hollywood, CA
Robert Rutan	Eye Witness LZ-129 Disaster Columbia, MD
Nap Salvail	Physical Materials Testing Expert NASA Kennedy Space Center, FL
Dr. S. R. Scaggs	Ballotechnic Behavior Expert Santa Fe, NM

Dr. Ulrich Schmidtchen	Peer Review/Coauthor Hindenburg paper Federal Institute for Materials Research and Testing Berlin, Germany
Mary Scilex	Researcher/Librarian Lakehurst Museum Lakehurst, NJ
Jan Seinkiner	Security Investigation Procedures Kennedy Space Center, FL
Dr. Darlene Slattery	Electron Microscope/ Spectroscopy Expert Hydrogen Research Division Florida Solar Energy Center Cocoa, FL
Dr. Jeremy Smallwood	Electrostatic Technologies/ESD/ Hazard Analysis Electrostatic Solutions London, United Kingdom
Debbi Smith	Hydrogen Expert/ Manuscript Review and Editing National Hydrogen Association Washington, DC
Alex Spencer	Reference Archivist Air and Space Museum Washington, DC
Albert Stoffler	Steward, Hindenburg Flights Friedrickshafen, Germany

Larry Sullivan	Aircraft Flight Experiences (atmospheric), Renown Aviation Santa Maria, CA
Dr. Sandy Thomas	Hydrogen Expert/Consultant Directed Technologies, Inc Arlington, VA
Walt Tomascak	Wildland Fire Behavior Missoula Technology Development Center, US Forest Service Missoula, MT
Judy Twigg	Hindenburg Photo Enhancing Broad Field Imaging Melbourne, FL
Dr. Martin Uman	Atmospheric Phenomena Expert Professor, University of Central Florida Gainesville, FL
Lee Underhill	Chemistry Consultant NASA Kennedy Space Center, FL
J. Gordon Vaeth	Airship Historian – Author Olympia, WA
Herman Van Dyk	German-English Translations Draftsman, LZ-129 drawings Peabody, MA
Richard Van Treuren	Airship Historian and Author Atlantis Productions Edgewater, FL

Dr. William Van Vorst

Peer Review/Coauthor
Hindenburg paper
Professor Emeritus, UCLA
Pacific Palisades, CA

Dr. T. Nejat Veziroglu

Peer Review Hindenburg paper
Professor, Clean Energy Research
Institute
University of Miami
Coral Gables, FL

Barbara Waibel

Archivarin
Zeppelin Museum
Friedrickshafen, Germany

Hepburn Walker, Jr.

Airship Expert (collector LZ-129
artifacts)
Navy Airshipman
Vero Beach, FL

Stanley Washburn

Eye Witness
LZ-129 Disaster
New York, NY

Captain George Watson

Eye Witness
LZ-129 Disaster
Lakehurst, NJ

Henry Wedaa

Explosives Expert (China Lake)
Diamond Bar, CA

Norbert Weinhold

VP Manufacturing/Engineering
Zeppelin Company
Friedrickshafen, Germany

Deiter Weil	Collector LZ Artifacts Berlin, Germany
Martha Williams	Infrared Spectroscopy Expert NASA Kennedy Space Center, FL
Charlie White	Hindenburg Movie Special Effects Paramount Pictures Port Orange, FL
Dianne Wood	Manuscript Assistance Florida Solar Energy Center Cocoa, FL
Karen Woods	Hindenburg Photo Colorization/ Characterization Marketing Talent Network Indian Harbor, FL
Don Woodward	Airship Historian and Author Editor of Aerostation San Diego, CA
Jim Wright	FBI Investigator Quantico, VA
Stan Young	Expert; Optical Microscopy, Scanning Electron Microscope, X-ray Energy Dispersive Spectroscopy NASA Kennedy Space Center, FL